D1447664

THE ★★★★
365
QUESTION
& ANSWER
QUIZ
BOOK

GYLES BRANDRETH

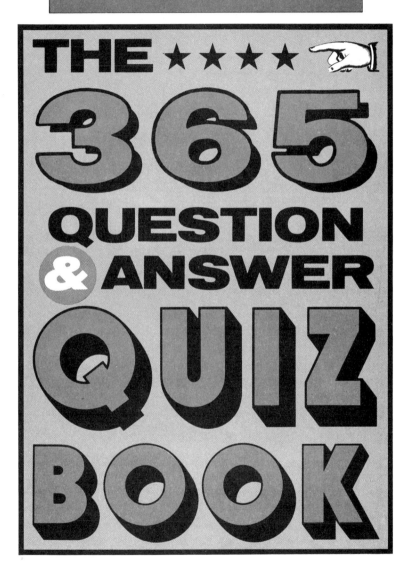

THE ★★★★ 365 QUESTION & ANSWER QUIZ BOOK

TREASURE PRESS

First published in Great Britain in 1977 by
Pelham Books Ltd, under the title *Pears All the Year Round Quiz Book*

This edition published in 1990 by
Treasure Press
Michelin House
81 Fulham Road
London SW3 6RB

Copyright © Gyles Brandreth 1977

Designed by John Elsegood

All Rights Reserved. No part of this publication may be reproduced, stored in a retrieval system, or transmitted, in any form or by any means, electronic, mechanical, photocopying, recording or otherwise, without the prior permission of the Copyright owner.

ISBN 1 85051 291 4

Produced in Czechoslovakia

50746

Contents

Four Questions
and Sixteen Answers
by way of Introduction

1. Why have I written this book?

Because a different quiz for every day of the year
seemed an irresistible idea.
Because I love reading quiz books.
Because I love writing them.
Because quiz books are so popular.

2. How should you use this book?

Start on 1 January and work your way through to 31
December.
Start on your birthday and work backwards through
the year.
Dip into any day you like and keep dipping.
Only look at the four alternative answers offered for
each question *after* you have tried to answer the
question without any clues. If you are awarding
yourself marks, you get five for every question
you can answer immediately, but only one for the
questions you answer when you have been given
all four possible answers.

3. What should you do if you find a mistake in the book?

Faint.

Recognise that nobody is perfect and that though I have checked all the facts very carefully it is just possible that an error or two has slipped past.

Send me a postcard at once so that I can put matters right as quickly as possible.

Accept my sincere apologies in advance.

4. What should you do if you have enjoyed this book?

Tell a friend.

Hold a Quiz Party and try out the questions on your guests.

Buy a dozen more copies as a hedge against inflation.

Have another drink!

GYLES BRANDRETH

P.S. In the Introduction you will find that *all* the answers are the right ones. When you tackle the 366 quizzes, you will find that only one in four of the possible answers is correct. The right answers to every question are listed at the back of the book.

Questions

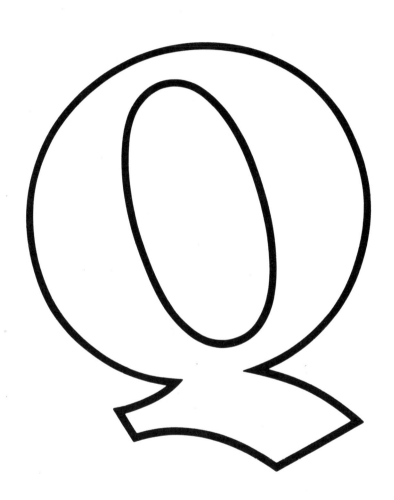

1 2 3 4 5 6 7

8 9 10 11 12 13 14

15 16 17 18 19 20 21

22 23 24 25 26 27 28

29 30 31

1 JANUARY

How long does it take for the earth to go round the sun?

> 30 days?
> 365 days?
> 366 days?
> 365.2422 days?

2 JANUARY

James Wolfe was born on 2 January 1727. He showed early promise in the Seven Years War and was given command of the expedition against Quebec, which he captured in spite of its strong position. He died on the expedition. In which year did it take place?

> 1747?
> 1759?
> 1776?
> 1802?

3 JANUARY

On 3 January 1795 one of the great English Potters died. At his Etruria works near Hanley he produced a new pottery ware to classical designs. What was his name?

Isiah Bone?
Louis Sèvres?
Billett Potter?
Josiah Wedgwood?

4 JANUARY

The French writer who wrote the essay *Le Mythe de Sisyphe,* the play *Caligula* and the novel *L'Etranger*, won the Nobel Prize for literature in 1957 and was killed in a car crash on 4 January 1960. What was his name?

Jean-Luc Godard?
Jean-Paul Sartre?
Albert Camus?
Robert Janvier?

5 JANUARY

On being asked what a clergyman had said in a sermon on the question of sin, a certain President of the United States answered, 'He said he was against it.' The President, who was born in 1872, died on 5 January 1933. What was his name?

> T. Woodrow Wilson?
> Calvin Coolidge?
> Warren G. Harding?
> Herbert Hoover?

6 JANUARY

Joan of Arc was born at Domrémy on 6 January 1412. She believed she had been called to save France from English domination and, through her efforts, Charles VII was crowned at Rheims in 1429. Captured by the English, she was burned as a heretic in 1431. In which year was she canonised?

> 1432?
> 1500?
> 1719?
> 1920?

7 JANUARY

To celebrate the birthday of writer, naturalist and animal-lover Gerald Durrell, who was born on 7 January 1925, a quiz with a four-legged flavour. The poll, the croup, the dock, the coronet, the hock, the gaskin, the stifle, the cannon and the elbow are all parts of which animal?

> The kangaroo?
> The cheetah?
> The cow or bull?
> The horse?

8 JANUARY

If you die today you can at least console yourself with the thought that you are in good company. On 8 January Catherine of Aragon died in 1536, Galileo died in 1642, Lord Baden-Powell died in 1941 and Chou En-lai died in 1976. In the year that Galileo died, the man whose laws of motion Galileo foresaw was born. What was this man's name?

> Thomas Fuller?
> Claudius Galen?
> Isaac Newton?
> Theodore Herzl?

9 JANUARY

Napoleon III, who came to power in France in the *coup d'état* of 1851 and during whose brief reign Paris was remodelled, died on 9 January 1873. He was married to the Empress Eugénie de Montijo of Spain. But who was his father?

> Napoleon I?
> Napoleon II?
> Napoleon I's brother Louis?
> Napoleon II's brother Henri?

10 JANUARY

The man who invented the revolver came from Hartford, Connecticut. He was born in 1814 and died on 10 January 1862. He invented the revolver when he was only twenty-one and its use was pioneered in the war with Mexico. What was the man's name?

> Sam Browne?
> Sam Colt?
> Sam Johnson?
> Sam Simeon?

11 JANUARY

'I like a story with a bad moral ... all good stories have a coarse touch or a bad moral, depend on't. If the story-tellers could ha' got decency and good morals from true stories, who'd have troubled to invent parables?' So said a great author in *Under the Greenwood Tree*. He was born in 1840 and died on 11 January 1928. What was his name?

> Rudyard Kipling?
> Henry James?
> Walter Scott?
> Thomas Hardy?

12 JANUARY

Another literary giant died today. In *Sparkling Cyanide* she wrote, 'The happy people are failures because they are on such good terms with themselves that they don't give a damn.' Hers was a happy life and a long one. Born in 1891, she died in 1976. What was her name?

> Agatha Christie?
> Ngaio Marsh?
> Dorothy L. Sayers?
> Daphne du Maurier?

13 JANUARY

James Joyce is the literary giant who died on 13 January 1941. Best known for his *Portrait of the Artist as a Young Man*, *Finnegans Wake* and *Ulysses*, he also wrote a play. What was it called?

> *Murder at the Vicarage?*
> *Exiles?*
> *A Spot of Bother?*
> *Stephen D?*

20

14 JANUARY

Edmund Halley, who died on 14 January 1742, was the second Astronomer Royal. Who was the first?

> Martin Ryle?
> John Flamsteed?
> John Pond?
> James Bradley?

15 JANUARY

The man who won the 1964 Nobel Peace Prize was born on 15 January 1929 and died in 1968. What was he called?

> Albert Schweitzer?
> U Thant?
> Martin Luther King?
> Bertrand Russell?

16 JANUARY

Edward Gibbon, who died on 16 January 1794, is still regarded by many as the greatest of all English historians. Born at Putney, the son of an MP, he travelled widely through Europe before publishing the first volume of his masterwork in 1776. What was it called?

> *The History of the World?*
> *Seven Pillars of Wisdom?*
> *The Decline and Fall of the Roman Empire?*
> *European History, Volume I?*

17 JANUARY

17 January was the birthday of two very different men: Anton Chekhov, who was born in 1860, and Lloyd George, who was born in 1863. David Lloyd George was Member of Parliament for Caernarvon from 1890 to 1944, but during which years was he Prime Minister?

> 1914-1920?
> 1916-1922?
> 1917-1919 and 1923-1927?
> 1918-1922 and 1931-1934?

18 JANUARY

Today is the day on which Scott reached the South Pole in 1912, and on which A.A. Milne (1882) and Danny Kaye (1913) were born. It's also the birthday of a great boxer, who first became World Heavyweight Boxing Champion in 1964. What's his name?

Floyd Patterson?
Sonny Liston?
Muhammad Ali?
Joe Frazier?

19 JANUARY

19 January is the birthday of the great American writer Edgar Allan Poe (1809) and the great Scottish engineer James Watt (1736). It also marks the birthday in 1839 of the French painter who said he wanted 'to make Impressionism something solid and durable, like the art of the museums'. You can see his famous painting *Les Grandes Baigneuses* in the National Gallery. What was his name?

Paul Cézanne?
Jean Millet?
Pierre Renoir?
Claude Monet?

20 JANUARY

King George V, who died on 20 January 1936, once remarked, 'I can't understand it. I'm really quite an ordinary sort of chap.' What occasion prompted this observation?

His Coronation in 1911?
The outbreak of the First World War in 1914?
The Prince of Wales' visit to Wales in 1927?
His Silver Jubilee in 1935?

21 JANUARY

The actor Paul Scofield was born in 21 January 1922. Lenin died on 21 January 1924. Eric Blair died on 21 January too, but in the year 1950. How was Eric Blair better known?

As Lord Haw-Haw?
As Stan Laurel?
As Stalin?
As George Orwell?

22 JANUARY

**Though the night was made for loving,
And the day returns too soon,
Yet we'll go no more a roving
By the light of the moon.**

Four famous lines from a famous poem by one of England's most famous poets. He was born on 22 January 1788. What was he called?

Byron?
Keats?
Shelley?
Wordsworth?

23 JANUARY

**Paul Robeson died on 23 January 1976. One hundred
and one years before, to the day, a very different man
died. The son of a clergyman, he was born in 1819 and
was writing sermons and poems at the age of four.
Later he became Professor of Modern History at
Cambridge and famous for his 'muscular Christianity'.
He wrote *Westward Ho!*. What was he called?**

Lewis Carroll?
Anthony Trollope?
Charles Kingsley?
John Masefield?

24 JANUARY

**Today is the Feast of St Timothy and the day on which
Lord Randolph Churchill died in 1895. 24 January is
also the birthday of Hadrian, the Roman Emperor who
visited Britain and built his wall between
Wallsend-on-Tyne and Bowness-on-Solway. Give or
take a few years, what were the dates of the Emperor
Hadrian?**

100–13 BC?
52 BC–AD 24?
AD 76–138?
AD 572–629?

25 JANUARY

Two great men of letters were born today. Robert Burns in 1759 and the other, who wrote *The Moon and Sixpence, Our Betters, The Constant Wife* and dozens more novels, plays and short stories in 1874. What was he called?

Noel Coward?
J.B. Priestley?
J.M. Barrie?
W. Somerset Maugham?

26 JANUARY

Today is Australia Day. Australia is made up of the Australian Capital Territory (Canberra), the Northern Territory and six states, of which five are New South Wales, Victoria, Queensland, South Australia, West Australia. What is the name of the sixth state?

Vermont?
Central Australia?
North West Australia?
Tasmania?

27 JANUARY

On 27 January Mozart was born (in 1756), Verdi died (in 1901), Charles Dodgson (alias Lewis Carroll) was born (in 1832) and, in 1926, a revolution in communications took place. What was it?

Samuel Morse invented his Morse Code?
The first message was sent by international telegraph?
The first use was made of Radar?
John Logie Baird demonstrated his first television pictures?

28 JANUARY

From being King of the Franks, he came to govern an empire comprising Gaul, Italy and large parts of Spain and Germany. He became Holy Roman Emperor. He was born in 742 and died on 28 January 814. Who was he?

Hannibal?
Charlemagne?
Tamburlaine?
Nero?

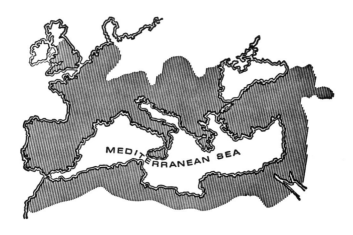

29 JANUARY

George III died on 29 January. So did Earl Haig. George III's death occurred in 1820, Earl Haig's in 1928. Haig was Commander-in-Chief in France from 1915 to 1919. What was the name of the controversial commander he replaced?

French?
Wavell?
Alexander?
Scott?

30 JANUARY

In 1649 and 1948 two totally different types of men were killed on 30 January. One was executed, the other was assassinated. Who were they?

Guy Fawkes and John F. Kennedy?
Thomas More and Kemal Atatürk?
Lord Darnley and William McKinley?
Charles I and Mahatma Gandhi?

31 JANUARY

31 January saw the completion of Nelson's column in Trafalgar Square in 1867, the death of the writer John Galsworthy in 1933, the death of the showman C.B. Cochran in 1951, and the birth, in 1797, of one of Austria's greatest composers, who died in poverty in Vienna at the early age of of thirty-one. What was his name?

Schumann?
Schubert?
Strauss?
Stravinsky?

ROBINSONS, BRISTOL. (10)

TRAFALGAR SQUARE.

1 2 3 4 5 6 7

8 9 10 11 12 13 14

15 16 17 18 19 20 21

22 23 24 25 26 27 28

29

1 FEBRUARY

In 1934 Arsenal were the League Champions, Manchester City were the FA Cup Winners, Italy won the World Cup, and one of England's best-known football players played for his country for the first time. He was born on 1 February 1915. What was his name?

Bobby Charlton?
Jimmy Hill?
Stanley Matthews?
Matt Busby?

2 FEBRUARY

When Mr Selwyn Lloyd retired as Speaker of the House of Commons on 2 February 1976, who succeeded him?

Horace King?
George Thomas?
Emmanuel Shinwell?
George Strauss?

3 FEBRUARY

3 February marks the birth of the composer Mendelssohn in 1809 and the death, in 1924, of the American President whose Administration introduced prohibition and women's suffrage and who said, 'The world must be made safe for democracy.' What was his name?

> William H. Taft?
> Woodrow Wilson?
> Theodore Roosevelt?
> Grover Cleveland?

6

4 FEBRUARY

On 4 February Thomas Carlyle died in 1881 and Roger Livesey died in 1976. What did each of them do that made them famous?

> Both were doctors?
> One was an historian and the other an architect?
> One was Archbishop of Canterbury and the other discovered plutonium?
> One was an author and the other an actor?

5 FEBRUARY

Born on 5 February 1788, this English Conservative statesman first held office in 1811 and is best remembered as the founder of the London police force. He died in a riding accident in 1850. What was his name?

Lord Palmerston?
Sir Robert Peel?
William Pitt?
William Gladstone?

6 FEBRUARY

The day that marks the accession of Elizabeth II in 1952, and of James II in 1685, also happens to be New Zealand Day. On which of the islands that form New Zealand is the capital city of Wellington to be found?

North Island?
South Island?
Stewart Island?
Chatham Island?

7 FEBRUARY

On 7 February 1812 was born the novelist whose many creations included Miss Miggs, Simon Tappertit, Mrs Jellyby, Mr Snagsby, Mrs Gummidge, Major Bagstock, Mrs Skewton, Mark Tapley, Mr Pecksniff, Mrs Gamp, Miss La Creevy, Mrs Kenwigs, Mr Boffin, Mr Blotton, Mr Stiggins and countless others. What was the writer's name?

William Makepeace Thackeray?
Nathaniel Hawthorne?
Mark Twain?
Charles Dickens?

8 FEBRUARY

Robert Burton, author of *The Anatomy of Melancholy* was born on 8 February 1577. Jules Verne, author of *Around the World in Eighty Days* was born on 8 February 1828. John Ruskin was born on 8 February 1819. What did John Ruskin do that made him famous?

He scored England's first-ever Test century in 1843?
He built the Ritz Hotel in Paris?
He invented the refracting telescope?
He was an art critic?

9 FEBRUARY

Lord Darnley, who was murdered on 9 February 1567, had a son who became King. Which King?

James I?
James II?
Louis XIII?
Ferdinand of Austria?

10 FEBRUARY

'It is the duty of Her Majesty's government neither to flap nor to falter.' 'I have never found in a long experience of politics that criticism is ever inhibited by ignorance.' 'When you're abroad you're a statesman; when you're at home you're just a politician.' Three of the many memorable sayings of this English politician and statesman who was born on 10 February 1894. What was his name?

Anthony Eden?
Winston Churchill?
R.A. Butler?
Harold Macmillan?

11 FEBRUARY

Sir Vivian Fuchs, who was born on 11 February 1908, led a British Commonwealth Expedition in 1957-1958 that achieved a very notable 'first'. What was it?

The first crossing of the Antarctic continent?
The first ascent of the North Face of Mount Everest?
The first circumnavigation of the globe in under 100 days?
The first crossing of the Arctic ocean?

12 FEBRUARY

The man who coined the phrase 'government of the people, by the people and for the people' was born on 12 February 1809 (the same day, incidentally, on which Charles Darwin was born). What was his name?

> Karl Marx?
> Friedrich Engels?
> Benjamin Disraeli?
> Abraham Lincoln?

13 FEBRUARY

Richard Wagner, the composer, died on 13 February 1883. Georges Simenon, the writer, was born on 13 February 1903. What was the name of his most famous detective?

> Poirot?
> Dubois?
> Maigret?
> Clouseau?

14 FEBRUARY

In case you didn't get a Valentine card today, console yourself with the thought that 'the course of true love never did run smooth'. Who first said that?

> William Shakespeare?
> Lord Byron?
> Elizabeth Barrett Browning?
> Rupert Brooke?

15 FEBRUARY

Sir Ernest Shackleton, the explorer whose expedition of 1909 reached within a hundred miles of the South Pole, was born on 15 February 1874. Thirteen years later, on 15 February 1887, H.M. Bateman was born. What did he do that made him famous?

> He invented the cathode ray tube?
> He was a pioneer aviator?
> He invented bi-focal lenses for spectacles?
> He was a cartoonist?

16 FEBRUARY

G.M. Trevelyan, who was born on 16 February 1876, is probably even more famous than H.M. Bateman. But what did he do?

> He was a painter?
> He was a motorcar manufacturer?
> He was an historian?
> He was a geologist?

17 FEBRUARY

Remembered particularly for his Shylock, his Lear, his Volpone and his Tamburlaine, this English actor-manager was born in 1902 and died on 17 February 1968. What was his name?

> Sir Henry Irving?
> Sir Johnston Forbes-Robertson?
> Sir Donald Wolfit?
> Sir Gerald du Maurier?

18 FEBRUARY

Hier stehe ich, ich kann nicht anders - 'Here I stand, I cannot do otherwise.' Those words were spoken at the Diet of Worms in 1521 by a man who died on 18 February 1546. What was his name?

Johann von Goethe?
King Sigismund?
Martin Luther?
Edward Westermarck?

19 FEBRUARY

Prince Andrew, the Queen's second son, was born on 19 February 1960. David Garrick, the English actor-manager, was born on 19 February 1717. Also born on 19 February, but back in 1473, was the founder of modern astronomy and author of *On the Revolution of the Celestial Orbs*. What was his name?

Nicolas Copernicus?
Galileo?
Sir John Herschel?
Johann Kepler?

20 FEBRUARY

Baruch Spinoza was born in Amsterdam in 1632 and died on 20 February 1677. What was he that has made him famous?

> An alchemist?
> A diplomat?
> A navigator?
> A philosopher?

21 FEBRUARY

Nikolai Gogol, who died on 21 February 1852, wrote a novel dealing with the malpractices involved in the supposed purchase of dead serfs. What was the novel called?

> *Death in Venice?*
> *When We Dead Awaken?*
> *Dead Souls?*
> *Dead Men Tell No Lies?*

22 FEBRUARY

'Father, I cannot tell a lie. I did it with my little hatchet.' The man believed to have spoken those immortal words was born on 22 February 1732. What was his name?

Benjamin Franklin?
Grinling Gibbons?
The Duke of Wellington?
George Washington?

2

23 FEBRUARY

Samuel Pepys, best known and most loved of all the great English diarists, was born on 23 February 1633. His famous diary, which he wrote in his own special code which was not deciphered until 1825, covered nine years of his life. Which nine years?

1653–1662?
1660–1669?
1671–1680?
1692–1701?

24 FEBRUARY

**In his Preface to the *Family Shakespeare*, the man who
expurgated the plays of Shakespeare promised his
readers that 'those expressions are omitted which
cannot with propriety be read aloud in the family.'
What is the name of this censorious individual, who
died on 24 February 1825 and who has given his name
to the language?**

> Samuel Johnson?
> Ralph Reader?
> Thomas Bowdler?
> Nathaniel Edit?

25 FEBRUARY

**On 25 February 1958 CND was launched. What was
CND?**

> The prototype of the Blue Streak rocket?
> The new number plates to be placed on diplomats'
> cars?
> The Currency Numerator Dial system?
> The Campaign for Nuclear Disarmament?

26 FEBRUARY

A French poet, dramatist and novelist whose most famous work is probably *Les Misérables* was born on 26 February 1802. He was also a graphic artist of note and left France to live in Guernsey. What was his name?

> Victor Hugo?
> Gustave Flaubert?
> Emile Zola?
> Benjamin Constant?

27 FEBRUARY

27 February was a good day for two American writers but a bad day for one English one. Henry Wadsworth Longfellow was born on 27 February 1807 and John Steinbeck was born on the same day in 1902. John Evelyn, however, died on 27 February 1706. What kind of literary endeavour is he remembered for?

> His poetry?
> His plays?
> His novels?
> His diary?

28 FEBRUARY

The relief of Ladysmith took place on 28 February 1900. Who or what was Ladysmith?

> Ladysmith was a colonel in the Indian Army who was wrongly court-marshalled, but eventually released?
> Lady Smith was the Home Secretary's wife in 1900 who was cured of St Vitus's dance?
> Ladysmith was a town in Texas that was overrun by Indians?
> Ladysmith was a town in South Africa besieged during the Boer War?

29 FEBRUARY

There is another word used to describe a Leap Year. What is it?

Bissextile?
Gratulatory?
Februrarian?
Lepidoptal?

1 2 3 4 5 6 7
8 9 10 11 12 13 14
15 16 17 18 19 20 21
22 23 24 25 26 27 28
29 30 31

1 MARCH

St David's Day is a day for wearing leeks and daffodils and for answering a Welsh quiz question. Wales is bounded by England to the East, the Bristol Channel to the South and the Irish Sea to the North. What flanks Wales to the West?

St David's Channel?
St George's Channel?
St Andrew's Channel?
St Patrick's Channel?

2 MARCH

D.H. Lawrence died on 2 March 1930, two years after completing *Lady Chatterley's Lover*. When was the complete novel first published in the United Kingdom?

1928?
1950?
1960?
1966?

c

3 MARCH

3 March has been a good day for the arts. Vincent van Gogh was born on 3 March 1853 and Sir Henry Wood was born on the same day in 1869. Sir Henry Wood made a unique contribution to the world of music. What was it?

He invented the modern trumpet?
He composed the music for the National Anthem?
He founded the London Symphony Orchestra?
He founded the Promenade Concerts?

4 MARCH

The Royal National Lifeboat Institution is a voluntary organisation that maintains 122 fast inshore boats and 135 lifeboats around the coasts of Britain and Ireland. It was founded on 4 March. In which year?

1824?
1900?
1937?
1953?

State Flag

5 MARCH

Joseph Vissarionovich Djugashvili died on 5 March 1953. How was he better known?

    As Lenin?
    As Trotsky?
    As Stalin?
    As Bulganin?

6 MARCH

The six thousand square feet of the ceiling of the Sistine Chapel were painted by a man who was born on 6 March 1475. What was his name?

    Raphael?
    Leonardo da Vinci?
    Titian?
    Michelangelo?

7 MARCH

Sir Edwin Landseer was born on 7 March 1802. For what work is he probably best remembered?

For designing Birmingham Cathedral?
For his painting of the Duke of Wellington?
For designing the lions in Trafalgar Square?
For designing the Albert Memorial?

8 MARCH

On 8 March 1973 one person was killed and 238 were injured in two bomb blasts in one of Europe's capital cities. Which one?

Paris?
Bonn?
London?
Rome?

9 MARCH

The Florentine explorer Amerigo Vespucci, after whom America was named, was born on 9 March 1451. On 9 March 1934 Yuri Gagarin was born. In 1961 he became the first man in space when he went on a flight that lasted one hour and forty-eight minutes. What was his spacecraft called?

Vostok 1?
Soyuz 1?
Apollo 1?
Sputnik 1?

10 MARCH

Prince Edward, the Queen's youngest son, was born on 10 March 1964. On 10 March 1872 Sergei Diaghilev was born. For what achievement is he famous?

> He assassinated Trotsky?
> He founded the Russian Ballet?
> He was the last Tsarist Prime Minister before the Revolution?
> He was an Impressionist painter?

11 MARCH

He is the Chancellor of Bradford University and the founder of the Open University. He was born on 11 March 1916. What's his name?

> Lord Franks?
> Lord Goodman?
> Sir Harold Wilson?
> Lord Vaizey?

12 MARCH

John Aubrey was born at Easton Piercey in Wiltshire on 12 March 1628. He was educated at Malmesbury Grammar School and Oxford University. He was an antiquary, eccentric and wit, portrayed on the stage in the 1960s and 1970s by the actor Roy Dotrice. For what work is John Aubrey remembered?

His *Poetics*?
His *Faerie Queene*?
His *Paradise Lost*?
His *Brief Lives*?

13 MARCH

'You ain't heard nothin' yet, folks', remarked Al Jolson in *The Jazz Singer*, one of the first talking films. The very first sound movie was shown in New York on 13 March. In which year?

1918?
1923?
1929?
1933?

14 MARCH

Admiral Byng was shot on 14 March 1757, Karl Marx died on 14 March 1883, Michael Caine was born on 14 March 1933, Michele Brown was born on 14 March 1947, and the mathematical physicist whose theory of relativity superseded Newton's theory of gravitation was born on 14 March 1879. What was he called?

      Blaise Pascal?
      Cornelius Drebbel?
      J.E. Lundstrom?
      Albert Einstein?

15 MARCH

The Ides of March mark the death of Julius Caesar in 44BC and the birth of Viscount Chandos in AD 1893. One of the auditoria at the new National Theatre in London is named after Lord Chandos. Which one?

      The Cottesloe?
      The Lyttelton?
      The Olivier?
      The Bayliss?

16 MARCH

Lord Beveridge, who died on 16 March 1963, was the author of the Beveridge Report. With what reform in British society did the Beveridge Report deal?

The nationalisation of the railways?
The formation of the social services?
The comprehensivisation of grammar schools?
The abolition of the death penalty?

17 MARCH

St Patrick's Day inevitably prompts an Irish question. Ulster has six counties. How many counties are there in Eire?

Six?
Ten?
Eighteen?
Twenty-six?

18 MARCH

This man, who died on 18 March 1745, is usually considered to have been Britain's first Prime Minister. What was his name?

Sir Robert Walpole?
Sir Robert Peel?
Lord North?
The Earl of Chatham?

19 MARCH

Sir Richard Burton, who was born on 19 March 1821, was a British explorer who made a pilgrimage to Mecca and Medina in 1853 disguised as a Muslim. He mastered some thirty-five different languages and is best remembered for his translation of one of the most famous of all anonymous works of literature. What was it?

The Bible?
The Arabian Nights?
The Koran?
The Kama Sutra?

20 MARCH

Born on 20 March 1828, he wrote plays about love, hate, marriage, emancipation and venereal disease. He died in 1906. What was he called?

Strindberg?
Ibsen?
Chekhov?
Pirandello?

21 MARCH

The man who composed the St Matthew and the St John Passion and the B Minor Mass was born at Eisenbach in Germany on 21 March 1685. What was his name?

> Beethoven?
> Bach?
> Mozart?
> Haydn?

22 MARCH

Goethe died on 22 March 1832. Stendhal died ten years later to the day. Both men were famous - but as what?

> As revolutionaries?
> As the inventors of the steam locomotive?
> As writers?
> As French generals?

23 MARCH

Sir Roger Bannister, who was born on 23 April 1929, once ran the mile in 3 minutes 59.4 seconds. It had been run in 4 minutes 12.75 seconds in 1884 and was run in 3 minutes 49.4 seconds in 1975, but in which year did Bannister make his historic run which broke the 4 minute barrier?

> 1949?
> 1952?
> 1954?
> 1958?

24 MARCH

Watch how you go on 24 March. It seems to be a day for dying. On 24 March Elizabeth I died in 1603, Longfellow died in 1882, Queen Mary died in 1953 and Lord Montgomery of Alamein died in 1976. On the very same day as Montgomery died, E.H. Shepard died. For what was he famous?

He invented the hovercraft?
He was Concorde's first pilot?
He illustrated *Winnie the Pooh*?
He was Poet Laureate?

25 MARCH

Bela Bartok was born on 25 March 1881. He was a Hungarian who died in 1945. For what was he famous?

He performed the first heart transplant?
He plotted to kill Hitler during the Second World War?
He was an architect?
He was a composer?

26 MARCH

26 March is another bad day for deaths. The composer Beethoven died on 26 March 1827, the American poet Walt Whitman died in 1892, the empire-builder Cecil Rhodes died in 1902, and Sir John Vanbrugh died in 1726. Vanbrugh was a playwright and architect. Which famous British building did he design?

Buckingham Palace?
Blenheim Palace?
Lambeth Palace?
The Victoria Palace?

27 MARCH

When did James Callaghan, who was born on 27 March 1912, become Prime Minister?

> October 1973?
> April 1975?
> April 1976?
> January 1977?

28 MARCH

The Princess Royal, Princess Victoria Alexandra Alice Mary, died on 28 March 1965. She was married to the 6th Earl of Harewood. Who was her father?

> George V?
> George VI?
> Prince Andrew of Greece?
> The Duke of Connaught?

29 MARCH

What happened to Alaska on 29 March 1867?

It suffered a severe earthquake?
It declared its independence?
It was covered by a snowpack?
It was sold to the United States by Russia?

30 MARCH

The Spanish painter Goya was born on 30 March 1746. What happened to his painting *The Duke of Wellington* in 1961?

It was destroyed by fire?
It was sold to the Metropolitan Museum of Art for a record sum?
It was revealed to be the work of Velasquez?
It was stolen from the National Gallery in London and not recovered until 1965?

31 MARCH

**The painter John Constable died on 31 March 1837.
The poet and divine John Donne died on the same day
in 1631. What special clerical office did Donne hold?**

He was Archbishop of Canterbury?
He was Cardinal Archbishop of Westminster?
He was Dean of St Paul's?
He was Bishop of Chichester?

1 2 3 4 5 6 7

8 9 10 11 12 13 14

15 16 17 18 19 20 21

22 23 24 25 26 27 28

29 30

1 APRIL

Ephraim Bomquist, the man who invented the tea-cup with the detachable handle that can be used by either left- or right-handed tea drinkers, was born on 1 April 1883 in Brooklyn, New York, USA. In which year was his invention patented?

> 1904?
> 1920?
> 1948?
> 1977?

2 APRIL

2 April saw the birth of Hans Christian Andersen, the Danish writer, in 1805, and the death of Georges Pompidou, the French President, in 1974. One of Britain's most distinguished actors was also born on 2 April in 1914. He made his first film appearance as Herbert Pocket in *Great Expectations* and his many other films have included *Oliver Twist, Father Brown* and *Cromwell*. What's his name?

> Sir Bernard Miles?
> Sir Richard Attenborough?
> Sir Michael Redgrave?
> Sir Alec Guinness?

3 APRIL

The man who built London's Savoy theatre and produced the operas of Gilbert and Sullivan was born in 1844 and died on 3 April 1901. What was his name?

Paul Raymond?
Prince Littler?
Vivian Van Dam?
Richard D'Oyly Carte?

4 APRIL

Sir Francis Drake was one of England's greatest seamen. Between 1577 and 1580 he sailed around the world, and on 4 April 1581 he was knighted by Queen Elizabeth I. What was the name of the boat in which he circumnavigated the globe?

The Golden Hind?
The Hispaniola?
Morning Cloud?
Hesperus?

5 APRIL

**Time turns the old days to derision,
Our loves into corpses or wives.**

So wrote a poet who was born on 5 April 1837. The poem was called 'Dolores'. His other famous verses include 'Itylus', 'Hertha', and 'Ave atque Vale'. He died in 1909. What was his name?

Samuel Taylor Coleridge?
Algernon Charles Swinburne?
Alfred Lord Tennyson?
Walter de la Mare?

6 APRIL

Raphael, the youngest of the three great artists of the High Renaissance, died on 6 April 1520. To see his *Madonna with the Goldfinch*, you must visit the Uffizi Gallery. In which European city will you find it?

Rome?
Venice?
Florence?
Madrid?

7 APRIL

If you thought 5 April's poetic quiz was too difficult, you may think today's too easy. 7 April marks the birthday, in 1770, of a poet who loved Spring, cuckoos, nightingales, skylarks, butterflies, daffodils and Milton:

> Milton! thou shouldst be living at this hour:
> England hath need of thee.

Who was the poet?

> William Cowper?
> William Wordsworth?
> William Blake?
> William Langland?

8 APRIL

'The beautiful doesn't matter to me', said one of the most versatile artists of all time, whose many extraordinary achievements included originating Cubism (with Braque), painting a mural called *Guernica* and dying, on 8 April 1973, the world's wealthiest artist. What was his name?

> Salvador Dali?
> Raoul Dufy?
> Pablo Picasso?
> Henri Matisse?

9 APRIL

9 April marks the deaths of Edward IV (able but dissolute Yorkist) in 1483 and Francis Bacon (who didn't write Shakespeare) in 1626, and the opening of London's National Gallery in 1838. On 9 April 1806 the man who built the Clifton Suspension Bridge and the liner *Great Britain* was born. What was his name?

> Isambard Kingdom Brunel?
> John Justin Fanshawe?
> Arthur Edward Phillips?
> James Robertson Justice?

10 APRIL

The famous last words of William Hazlitt, who was born on 10 April 1778 and who died in 1830, were, 'Well, I've had a happy life.' Whose were the even more famous last words, 'Die, my dear doctor, that's the last thing I shall do!'?

> Viscount Palmerston?
> Harpo Marx?
> Marie Stopes?
> Edward VII?

11 APRIL

The Treaty of Utrecht, signed on 13 April 1713, ended a European war which had started in 1702. Which war?

The War of the Spanish Succession?
The Great War?
The Seven Years War?
The Spanish Civil War?

12 APRIL

Franklin D. Roosevelt became President of the United States in 1933. He was still President when he died on 12 April 1945. Who was his successor?

Herbert Hoover?
Dwight Eisenhower?
Harry Truman?
Warren Harding?

13 APRIL

F.W. Woolworth was born on 13 April 1852. The shop assistants in Woolworth's are noted for their quick wits. If you told one to add 8 to a certain number, subtract 8 from the sum, multiply the remainder by 8, and divide the product by 8, she would tell you 4 was the answer. What would the 'certain number' have been ?

4?
8?
96?
868?

14 APRIL

On 14 April the composer Handel died in 1759 and the actor Sir John Gielgud was born in 1904. In the plays *Home* by David Storey and *No Man's Land* by Harold Pinter, who co-starred with Gielgud?

Sir John Mills?
Sir Lewis Casson?
Sir John Clements?
Sir Ralph Richardson?

15 APRIL

The SS *Titanic* sank on 15 April 1912. Why?

She was attacked by German warships?
She collided with an iceberg?
She caught fire?
It is a mystery that has never been solved?

16 APRIL

Sir Charles Chaplin was born on 16 April 1889, just four days before Adolf Hitler. In which of his films did Chaplin impersonate Hitler?

Modern Times?
City Lights?
The Gold Rush?
The Great Dictator?

17 APRIL

John Ford, the Jacobean dramatist, was baptised on 17 April 1586. In the same year, a royal arrest and trial took place at Fotheringhay Castle in Northamptonshire. Who was arrested and tried?

Elizabeth I?
Mary Queen of Scots?
Philip II of Spain?
John III of Sweden?

18 APRIL

On 18 April 1881 the Natural History Museum in London's South Kensington was opened. On 18 April 1689, at the Tower of London, the English judge who held the 'bloody assize' after Monmouth's unsuccessful rebellion died. What was his name?

Lord Goddard?
Lord Denning?
Lord Jeffreys?
Lord Parker?

19 APRIL

On 19 April 1824 the poet Byron died. Two years later to the day Sir Squire Bancroft died. What did he do?

With Elisha G. Otis he developed the passenger lift?
He was the first brain surgeon?
He was an actor-manager?
He was a Whig Prime Minister?

20 APRIL

20 April 1889 was the birthday of Adolf Hitler. 1889 saw a much happier event, when a structure, 985 feet high, was completed at the heart of one of Europe's largest cities. What was it?

The Post Office Tower in London?
The Blackpool Tower?
The Leaning Tower of Pisa?
The Eiffel Tower in Paris?

21 APRIL

On 21 April 1926 Queen Elizabeth II was born. Where?

At Buckingham Place?
At Sandringham House, Norfolk?
At Clarence House?
At 17 Bruton Street, London W.1?

22 APRIL

On 22 April 1916 the violinist Yehudi Menuhin was born in New York. On 22 April 1707 the novelist Henry Fielding was born at Sharpham Park near Glastonbury. In the 1963 film of Fielding's _Tom Jones_, who played the part of the hero?

Peter Firth?
Jim Dale?
Albert Finney?
David Hemmings?

23 APRIL

William Shakespeare was baptised on 26 April 1564. It is possible that he was born on 23 April 1564. It is certain he died on 23 April 1616. Your question for this St George's Day is: what was the name of the actor who first played Othello, Hamlet, King Lear and other parts at the Globe in London?

Richard Burton?
Richard Roundtree?
Richard Burbage?
Richard Neville?

24 APRIL

One of England's most successful novelists - he is reckoned to have earned £70,000 from his writing and that a hundred years ago! - was born on 24 April 1815. He was the author of *Barchester Towers*. What was his name?

Charles Dickens?
Thomas Hardy?
Joseph Conrad?
Anthony Trollope?

25 APRIL

The Feast of St Mark is also the birthday of Edward II in 1284 (he came to the throne in 1307 and was murdered in 1327) and since 1916 has been known as ANZAC Day. What does ANZAC mean?

Army and Navy Zoological Auxiliary Committee?
Anti-Nazi Action Committee?
Australian and New Zealand Army Corps?
It was the nickname given to Lord Kitchener by his men?

26 APRIL

1731, the year in which Daniel Defoe, the author of *Robinson Crusoe*, died on 26 April, was a special year for the English Prime Minister. Why?

He was assassinated?
He was appointed Viceroy of India?
He called the first-ever General Election?
He took up residence at 10 Downing Street?

Edward II

27 APRIL

Edward Gibbon, the historian, was born on 27 April 1737. Samuel Morse, who devised the Morse Code, was born on 27 April 1791. Using the dots(.) and dashes(-) of the Morse Code, how would you send the emergency message SOS?

         ... --- ... ?
         .- .- .- ?
         . --------- . ?
         ---- ... ---- ?

28 APRIL

On 28 April 1876 Queen Victoria became Empress of India. On 28 April 1945 Benito Mussolini died. How?

He was hanged by the Allied Forces after his trial in Rome?
He committed suicide?
He was shot while attempting to escape to Switzerland?
He was run over by a tank?

29 APRIL

Sir Thomas Beecham, the great conductor, was born on 29 April 1879. A century before, on 29 April 1779, a notorious mutiny took place aboard the ship *The Bounty*. Who was the Captain of *The Bounty*?

Captain Cook?
Captain Cavallo?
Captain Christian?
Captain Bligh?

30 APRIL

**Queen Juliana of the Netherlands was born on 30 April
1909. In 1937 she married Prince Bernhard of Lippe-
Biesterfeld. In connection with accepting money from
which international company did Prince Bernhard fall
from grace in 1976?**

British Leyland?
Lockheed?
Slater Walker Securities?
ICI?

1 2 3 4 5 6 7

8 9 10 11 12 13 14

15 16 17 18 19 20 21

22 23 24 25 26 27 28

29 30 31

1 MAY

**May Day is the Feast Day of St Philip and St James
and the day on which Doctor Livingstone died in 1873.
Around the world there are several places called
Livingstone. One of the most famous is near the North
bank of the Zambesi River, only seven miles from the
Victoria Falls. It was the capital of Northern Rhodesia
from 1907 to 1935. What is the present name of the
country in which this Livingstone is situated?**

> Angola?
> Zanzibar?
> Zambia?
> Kenya?

2 MAY

**The first woman Member of Parliament to take her
seat in the House of Commons died on 2 May 1964.
She was an American by birth and her maiden name
was Langhorne. By what name is she remembered?**

> Barbara Wootton?
> Emmeline Pankhurst?
> Bessie Braddock?
> Nancy Astor?

D

St Paul's Cathedral

3 MAY

**On May 3 1951 King George VI opened something
rather special on the steps of St Paul's Cathedral in
London. What was it?**

> The nation's Wedding Anniversary present to him
> and the Queen?
> The new National Theatre?
> The capital's first-ever one-way street?
> The Festival of Britain?

4 MAY

**The biologist T.H. Huxley, who coined the term
'agnostic', was born on 4 May 1825. The *Daily Mail*
was founded on 4 May 1896, a year after Huxley's
death. Eighty years later, what was the name of the
Daily Mail's celebrated diarist?**

> William Hickey?
> Bernard Levin?
> Charles Greville?
> Nigel Dempster?

5 MAY

Napoleon Bonaparte died on the island of St Helena on 5 May 1821. Previously he had been exiled on the island of Elba, and the phrase 'Able was I ere I saw Elba' is jokingly attributed to him. This can be read forwards or backwards. What is the technical term to describe such a phrase?

A palindrome?
An anagram?
A hobson-jobson?
An epithet?

6 MAY

A day of mixed blessings for the royal family (Edward VII died in 1910 and Princess Margaret got married in 1960), but a great day for philatelists (the first adhesive stamps were issued in 1840). In Moravia, on 6 May 1856, the founder of psychoanalysis was born. What was his name?

Carl Jung?
Sigmund Freud?
William Sargeant?
Anthony Fokker?

7 MAY

Today is a good day for musicians - Tchaikovsky was born in 1840 and the Royal College of Music was founded in 1883 - but a grim day for those who recall the First World War. On 7 May 1915, a German submarine sunk a very famous vessel. Her name?

SS *Titanic?*
SS *Jervis Bay?*
SS *Lusitania?*
SS *Rawalpindi?*

8 MAY

On 8 May 1873 John Stuart Mill, the English philosopher, died. On 8 May 1884 the American President was born who had a notice on his desk at the White House that read, 'The buck stops here.' What was his name?

John Quincy Adams?
Theodore Roosevelt?
Harry S. Truman?
Lyndon B. Johnson?

9 MAY

On May 9 1966 China exploded her third nuclear device. A happier event in 1966 was England's victory over West Germany in the World Cup soccer final. What was the score?

England 1 Germany 0 ?
England 2 Germany 1 ?
England 3 Germany 2 ?
England 4 Germany 2 ?

10 MAY

Sir Henry Stanley, who died on 10 May 1904, was commissioned by the *New York Herald* to find Dr Livingstone. He did so, greeting him with the now famous words, 'Dr Livingstone, I presume?' Where and when?

Ujiji in 1871?
Timbuctoo in 1880?
Cape Town in 1889?
Mombasa in 1901?

11 MAY

11 May is the date of the Battle of Fontenoy in 1745 and the birth of Israel Baline in 1888. Under a different name Baline wrote 'White Christmas', *Call Me Madam*, 'There's No Business Like Show Business' and many more hit songs and shows. What was his name?

Cole Porter?
Alan Jay Lerner?
Oscar Hammerstein?
Irving Berlin?

12 MAY

12 May marks the birthday of three eminent Victorians: Edward Lear (1812), Florence Nightingale (1820) and Dante Gabriel Rossetti (1828). One of them died in 1910, with 'Too kind! Too kind!' as his or her last words. Which of the three was it?

Edward Lear?
Florence Nightingale?
Dante Gabriel Rossetti?

13 MAY

This slow-speaking deep-thinking American film star, whose many pictures included *The Virginian* (1929), *Desire* (1936), *Sergeant York* (1941) and *High Noon* (1952), was born in 1901 and died on 13 May 1961. What was his name?

Alan Ladd?
Spencer Tracy?
Clark Gable?
Gary Cooper?

14 MAY

14 May marks the deaths of two writers, the Swedish Strindberg in 1912 and the English Rider Haggard in 1925, and the birth, in 1686, of Gabriel Daniel Fahrenheit, the German physicist who introduced the mercury thermometer and fixed thermometric standards. What is boiling point in the Fahrenheit scale?

32 degrees?
100 degrees?
144 degrees?
212 degrees?

15 MAY

Edmund Kean, the great actor, died on 15 May 1833. In 1971, which modern English actor portrayed Kean on the London stage?

Laurence Olivier?
Paul Scofield?
Alan Badel?
Frank Finlay?

16 MAY

On 16 May 1905, at Rushden in Northamptonshire, a writer was born whose many novels and short stories included *The Fallow Land, The Jacaranda Tree* and *My Uncle Silas*. Many of his stories of service life were published under the name 'Flying-Officer X'. What was his real name?

Evelyn Waugh?
H.E. Bates?
Anthony Powell?
E.M. Forster?

17 MAY

On 17 May 1976 who was Leader of the British Liberal Party? A week before he wasn't Leader.

> Jo Grimond?
> Jeremy Thorpe?
> David Steel?
> John Pardoe?

18 MAY

On 18 May Napoleon became Emperor in 1804 and the BBC was founded in 1922. 18 May 1919 marked the birthday of someone who became Madame Roberto de Arias. By what name is she known to the world?

> Dame Nellie Melba?
> Dame Anna Neagle?
> Dame Margot Fonteyn?
> Dame Margaret Rutherford?

19 MAY

'Wild agitator! Means well' was Lewis Carroll's ingenious anagram of the name of William Ewart Gladstone, who died on 19 May 1898. 'Aircraftsman Shaw' is not an anagram, but it is an assumed name. The man who assumed it was killed on his motorcycle on 19 May 1935. What was his real name?

T.S. Eliot?
e.e. Cummings?
A.A. Milne?
T.E. Lawrence?

20 MAY

Barbara Hepworth, the sculptress, died on 20 May 1975. Four centuries earlier, on 20 May 1506, a very different type of person also died. He was a Genoan navigator who discovered the Bahamas, Cuba and other West Indian islands in 1492 and who landed on the lowlands of South America in 1498. What was his name?

John Cabot?
Ferdinand Magellan?
Leif Ericsson?
Christopher Columbus?

21 MAY

Elizabeth Fry, the Quaker prison reformer, was born on 21 May 1780. On the same day in 1688, a poet was born whose most famous couplet is probably this one:

> **A little learning is a dang'rous thing;**
> **Drink deep, or taste not the Pierian spring.**

Who was the poet?

John Milton?
Alexander Pope?
Thomas Gray?
Edmund Spenser?

22 MAY

On 22 May 1859 Sir Arthur Conan Doyle was born. On 22 May 1931 Whipsnade Zoo in Bedfordshire was opened. On 22 May 1907 Laurence Olivier was born. Who is or was Lord Olivier's *second* wife?

Jill Esmond?
Vivien Leigh?
Joan Plowright?
Peggy Ashcroft?

23 MAY

Hugh Casson, the architect, was born on 23 May 1910. On 23 May 1937, John D. Rockefeller died at the age of ninety-eight. He was one of the world's richest men. How did he make his fortune?

He discovered uranium?
He invented cats' eyes used in road-making?
He founded the Standard Oil Company?
He founded General Motors?

24 MAY

Queen Victoria was born on 24 May 1819. Samuel Morse sent his first telegraphic message on 24 May 1844. And on 24 May 1941, the Royal Navy suffered one of the most terrible losses of the Second World War when one of its ships was sunk. Which ship?

HMS *Portsmouth?*
HMS *Valiant?*
HMS *Mountbatten?*
HMS *Hood?*

25 MAY

One of Britain's most admired television commentators was born on 25 May 1913. He is best remembered for his coverage of major Royal events and State occasions, and as the presenter of the BBC programme *Panorama*. What was his name?

Macdonald Hobley?
Huw Wheldon?
Cliff Michelmore?
Richard Dimbleby?

26 MAY

'My wife, who, poor wretch, is troubled with her lonely life', was what one famous man wrote in his diary on 19 December 1662. It certainly wasn't George V writing about his wife Queen Mary, who was born on 26 May 1867. It was a man who died on 26 May 1703. What was his name?

Paul Tanfield?
Richard Crossman?
Samuel Pepys?
John Evelyn?

27 MAY

27 May marks the sinking of the *Bismarck* in 1941 and the birth, in 1923, of the only American Secretary of State to win the Nobel Peace Prize. What is his name?

Cyrus Vance?
Henry Kissinger?
Dean Rusk?
Averell Harriman?

28 MAY

The Duke of Windsor, formerly King Edward VIII, died on 28 May 1972. From 1940 to 1945 what position did he hold?

> King?
> British Ambassador to the United States of America?
> Governor of the Bahamas?
> None?

29 MAY

29 May marks the capture of Constantinople in 1453, the conquest of Mount Everest five hundred years later, and, in between, the birth of King Charles II in 1630. Who were his parents?

> Charles I and Henrietta-Maria of France?
> James I and Anne of Denmark?
> Mary I and Philip II of Spain?
> James II and Lady Anne Hyde?

30 MAY

30 May marks the death of three extraordinary people. Joan of Arc was burned at the stake on 30 May 1431. Wilbur Wright, the pioneer airman, died on 30 May 1912. And François-Marie Arouet, who said 'If God did not exist we'd have to invent him' and much else besides, died on 30 May 1778. How was he better known?

> Voltaire?
> Molière?
> Corneille?
> Racine?

31 MAY

William Heath Robinson, illustrator, cartoonist and creator of fantastical machines, was born on 31 May 1872. The Battle of Jutland also took place on 31 May, but in which year?

1685?
1776?
1854?
1916?

1 2 3 4 5 6 7

8 9 10 11 12 13 14

15 16 17 18 19 20 21

22 23 24 25 26 27 28

29 30

1 JUNE

John Masefield, who was born on 1 June 1878, was Poet Laureate until his death on 12 May 1967, when he was succeeded by Cecil Day-Lewis, who was succeeded on his death by Sir John Betjeman. Who, traditionally, is said to be the first English Poet Laureate?

John Dryden?
Ben Jonson?
Sir William D'Avenant?
Colley Cibber?

2 JUNE

2 June marks the birth of Thomas Hardy in 1840 and the coronation of Elizabeth II in 1953. 1953 also saw a famous fraud exposed. In 1912, a skull said to be over 50,000 years old was discovered. It was nothing of the sort, but the hoax went unexploded for half a century. Where was the skull discovered?

Romney Marsh?
Castle Combe?
Pilt Down?
Over Wallop?

3 JUNE

3 June marks the birth of George V in 1865 and the death of Pope John XXIII in 1963. Samuel Plimsoll, the English social reformer, also died on 3 June, in 1898. What is or was the Plimsoll Line?

A row of sports shoes?
The place where the date changes as you cross the Equator?
The line above which no ship must sink while loading?
The line that marks true North on a compass?

4 JUNE

On 4 June 1738 George III was born. Sixty years later to the day, Italy's lustiest adventurer, Giacomo Casanova de Seingalt, died. When Casanova's life was turned into a television series by the BBC, who played the part of Casanova?

Frank Finlay?
Richard O'Sullivan?
Edward Woodward?
Orson Welles?

5 JUNE

On 5 June 1783 the French brothers Joseph and Jacques Montgolfier became airborne. Their craft managed to fly six miles. What kind of craft was it?

An aeroplane?
An airship?
A balloon?
A hovercraft?

6 JUNE

6 June 1944 was D Day, the day of the invasion of Europe. How many ships were there in the invasion fleet?

> Over 500?
> Over 1000?
> Over 4000?
> Over 10,000?

7 JUNE

7 June marks the birthdays of the painter Gauguin, in 1848, and the writer R.D. Blackmore, in 1825, and the death, in 1329, of the warrior Scot who fought Edward I and Edward II of England and himself became King of Scotland in 1306. What was his name?

> Robert Bruce?
> Robert Stewart?
> Robert Burns?
> Rob Roy?

8 JUNE

Sir John Millais was born on 8 June 1829. Why is he famous?

> He was the first man to run 100 yards in under 10 seconds?
> He invented the internal combustion engine?
> He was Queen Victoria's tutor?
> He was an artist?

9 JUNE

George Stephenson, who was born on 9 June 1781, won a £500 prize in 1829 when one of the locomotives he had designed travelled at 30 miles per hour. What was the name of the locomotive?

> *Locomotion?*
> *Rocket?*
> *Great Britain?*
> *Darlington?*

10 JUNE

HRH The Prince Philip, Duke of Edinburgh, Earl of Merioneth and Baron Greenwich, KG, PC, KT, OM, GBE, was born on 10 June 1921. Who were his parents?

Prince Andrew of Greece and Princess Alice of Battenberg?
The Duke of Fife and the Hon. Caroline Dewar?
King Paul I of Greece and Princess Frederica of Brunswick?
Prince Oscar and Countess von Ruppin?

11 JUNE

John Constable, the English landscape painter, was born on 11 June in a momentous year. It was the year of the American War of Independence, of Cook's third voyage of discovery, of David Garrick's last appearance as an actor and of the first St Leger horse race run at Doncaster. What was the year?

1699?
1740?
1776?
1805?

12 JUNE

Anthony Eden, who was British Prime Minister from 1955 to 1957, was born on 12 June 1897. He died in 1977. In 1961 an earldom was conferred upon him. What was the name of Eden's earldom?

> Cawdor?
> Aylesford?
> Swinton?
> Avon?

13 JUNE

W.B. Yeats, the poet, was born on 13 June 1865. Thomas Arnold, churchman, author and headmaster, was born on 13 June 1795. He died on 12 June 1842. From 1818 until the year of his death, Arnold was headmaster of which famous public school?

> Eton?
> Winchester?
> Rugby?
> Harrow?

14 JUNE

14 June marks the date of the Battle of Naseby in 1645 and the death of Jerome K. Jerome, author of _Three Men in a Boat_, in 1927. The Scottish inventor of the televisor and the noctovisor died on 14 June 1946. What was his name?

John Logie Baird?
Robert Watson-Watt?
Thomas Alva Edison?
Kirkpatrick Macmillan?

15 JUNE

In 1215, 15 June saw the signing of the Magna Carta. In 1843 it saw the birth of the Norwegian composer Grieg. And in 1919 it saw the first flight across the Atlantic, made by Sir John Alcock and Sir Arthur Brown. They flew from Newfoundland to Ireland. How long did they take?

8 hours 5 minutes?
16 hours 12 minutes?
21 hours 54 minutes?
27 hours 1 minute?

16 JUNE

George II was the last English monarch to lead his troops into battle. He did so on 16 June 1743. What was the battle called?

The Battle of Bunker Hill?
The Battle of Dettingen?
The Battle of Wakefield?
The Battle of Plassey?

17 JUNE

On 17 June 1967 which country exploded its first H Bomb?

France?
India?
China?
Egypt?

18 JUNE

Igor Stravinsky, the Russian composer who became a French citizen in 1934 and an American citizen in 1945, was born on 18 June 1882. On 18 June 1815 the Battle of Waterloo took place. In which country?

England?
France?
Belgium?
Austria?

THE DUKE OF WELLINGTON.

19 JUNE

'He was a bold man who first swallowed an oyster', said an English and Scottish King who was born on 19 June 1566. What was his name?

James I?
William III?
George I?
Edward VII?

20 JUNE

Niccolo Machiavelli, the Florentine Renaissance diplomat and theorist of the modern state, was born in 1467 and died on 20 June 1527. He wrote a book, dedicated to Lorenzo the Magnificent, about the realities of politics. What was it called?

Mein Kampf?
The Realities of Politics?
Utopia?
The Prince?

21 JUNE

On 21 June 1970 which country won the World Cup soccer contest?

West Germany?
England?
Brazil?
Italy?

22 JUNE

The Italian composer whose operas included *Tosca, La Bohème, Manon Lescaut* and *Madame Butterfly* was born on 22 June 1858. What was his name?

Puccini?
Verdi?
Gounod?
Wagner?

23 JUNE

Today marks the anniversary of the Battle of Plassey (1757), the birthdays of Edward VII (1894) and the cricketer Leonard Hutton (1916), and the death in 1875 of the inventor of the sewing machine. What was his name?

> Henry Robinson?
> Oscar Reel?
> Billy Cotton?
> Isaac Singer?

24 JUNE

The original W.H. Smith, in one of whose stores you may even have bought this book, was born on 24 June 1825, the anniversary of the Battle of Bannockburn, which took place in 1314. Which English king was defeated at Bannockburn?

> Stephen?
> Richard II?
> Edward II?
> Henry III?

25 JUNE

Earl Mountbatten of Burma was born on 25 June 1900. Fifty years later to the day the Korean War began. On 25 June 1876, a United States Cavalry officer and his men were surrounded and killed at the Battle of Little Big Horn. What was the officer's name?

> Colonel Boone?
> General Custer?
> Colonel Bogey?
> General Marshall?

26 JUNE

The United Nations Charter came into force on 26 June 1945. Who was Secretary-General of the UN from 1946 to 1952?

> Trygve Lie?
> Dag Hammarskjold?
> U Thant?
> Philip Guedalla?

27 JUNE

Helen Keller was born on 27 June 1880. She died in 1968. Why is she famous?

She was the first woman accepted into the Royal Air Force?
She pioneered the use of contraception among the poor in India and Pakistan?
She was a nurse who was arrested and shot by the Germans during the First World War?
She overcame overwhelming physical handicaps, including deafness and blindness, to become an author and lecturer?

28 JUNE

The Treaty of Versailles was signed on 28 June 1919. Who was the Treaty between?

The Allies and Germany?
The Allies and Austria?
The Allies and Bulgaria?
The Allies and Germany, Austria and Bulgaria?

29 JUNE

Sir Peter Paul Rubens was born on 29 June 1577. Antoine de Saint-Exupéry, author of *The Little Prince*, was born on 29 June 1900. Ignace Paderewski died on 29 June 1941. Why is his name famous?

He was a great pianist?
He was the first Prime Minister of modern Poland?
He won the Nobel Peace Prize in 1935?
He wrote 'Singing in the Rain'?

30 JUNE

The poetess Elizabeth Barrett Browning died on 30 June 1861. Before she married Robert Browning, Elizabeth and her family lived in one of London's best-known streets. Which one?

Oxford Street?
Wimpole Street?
Baker Street?
Kensington Church Street?

1 2 3 4 5 6 7
8 9 10 11 12 13 14
15 16 17 18 19 20 21
22 23 24 25 26 27 28
29 30 31

1 JULY

Today is Dominion Day in Canada, a country that is larger than even the United States of America. What is Canada's population?

> Around 20 million?
> Around 40 million?
> Around 60 million ?
> Around 71 million?

2 JULY

Today marks the anniversary of the Battle of Marston Moor in 1644 and the birth of Lord Home in 1903. As Sir Alec Douglas-Home, he succeeded Harold Macmillan as British Prime Minister. But in which year?

> 1959?
> 1963?
> 1965?
> 1967?

3 JULY

On 3 July 1941 Palmyra surrendered to the Allied forces. In which country would you find Palmyra (Tudmur)?

Syria?
Italy?
Burma?
Japan?

4 JULY

4 July marks American Independence in 1776. In which American city was the Declaration of Independence signed?

Washington D.C.?
Boston?
New York?
Philadelphia?

5 JULY

Georgette Heyer died on 5 July 1974. Why was Georgette Heyer famous?

She was a sculptress?
She was a novelist?
She was a tennis player?
She was an actress?

6 JULY

Beatrix Potter was born on 6 July 1866. Edward VI died on 6 July 1553. The Battle of Sedgemoor, at which the Duke of Monmouth's troops were routed by John Churchill and his army, took place on 6 July. In which year?

1485?
1585?
1685?
1785?

7 JULY

Edward I died on 7 July 1307. Sir Arthur Conan Doyle died on 7 July in the year when the BBC first attempted television broadcasts, when Seagrave was killed in a speedboat travelling on Lake Windermere at 100mph, when the airship R 101 was destroyed and when the government first rejected a scheme for a Channel tunnel. What year was it?

1930?
1935?
1938?
1947?

8 JULY

The French poet and fabulist, Jean de la Fontaine, was born in Champagne on 8 July 1621. The English poet who wrote 'To a Skylark', which begins 'Hail to thee, blithe Spirit!', died on 8 July 1822. What was his name?

> William Wordsworth?
> John Keats?
> Percy Bysshe Shelley?
> Thomas Hood?

9 JULY

The author of *Sailing: A Course of my Life* and *Music: A Joy for Life* was born on 9 July 1916. What is his name?

> Uffa Fox?
> Colin Davis?
> Edward Heath?
> Anthony Hopkins?

10 JULY

Today is the birthday of three very different writers. Frederick Marryatt was born on 10 July 1792. Marcel Proust was born on 10 July 1871. Edmund Bentley was born on 10 July 1875. Bentley gave his own second name to the pithy, witty verses that he wrote. What was his second name?

Limerick?
Haiku?
Epitaph?
Clerihew?

11 JULY

On 11 July 1536 Desiderius Erasmus died. Who was he?

A Dutch Renaissance humanist and author of *Praise of Folly?*
The compiler of *Hymns Ancient and Modern* and *Songs of Praise?*
The captain of the flagship that led the Spanish Armada?
The Portuguese navigator who discovered Peru?

12 JULY

12 July saw the birth of Julius Caesar in the year 100 BC and the death of the anti-Catholic agitator Titus Oates in 1705. Captain Dreyfus, who in 1894 was wrongly accused of divulging secrets to a foreign power and was not fully exonerated until 1906, also died on 12 July. In which year?

1907?
1912?
1920?
1935?

13 JULY

The English poet John Clare was born on 13 July 1793 and the French revolutionary Jean Paul Marat was murdered on 13 July 1793. Who killed Marat?

> Maximilien Robespierre?
> Marie Tussaud?
> Madeleine Renaud?
> Charlotte Corday?

14 JULY

Bastille Day in France (1789) is also the day on which Grock died in 1959. Who was Grock?

> He was a cartoonist?
> He was the youngest of the Marx Brothers,
> who only appeared in two of their zany films?
> He was a fashion designer?
> He was a clown?

15 JULY

Rembrandt the artist was born on this day, the Feast of St Swithin, in 1606. Marie Tempest the actress was born on the same day in 1866. What is the special tradition associated with St Swithin's Day?

> If it rains on St Swithin's Day it will rain for
> the next forty days?
> The first person you meet on St Swithin's morn
> will be the person you will marry?
> St Swithin's Day is the true date for Midsummer's
> Day?
> You should roll hard-boiled eggs down a hillside
> on St Swithin's Day?

16 JULY

Sir Joshua Reynolds, the English portrait painter, was born on 16 July 1723. Roald Amundsen was born on 16 July 1872. Why is he famous?

He made the first successful ascent of Mont Blanc?
He built the Tay Bridge in Scotland?
He beat Scott in the race to reach the South Pole in 1911?
He was captain of the first Australian team to win the Ashes?

17 JULY

When Oscar Wilde said, 'I wish I'd said that!' he replied, 'You will, Oscar, you will.' In answer to the question, 'For two days' labour you ask two hundred guineas?' he replied, 'No, I ask it for the knowledge of a lifetime.' In *The Gentle Art of Making Enemies* he wrote, 'I am not arguing with you - I am telling you.' He died on 17 July 1903. Who was he?

Aubrey Beardsley?
James McNeill Whistler?
Lord Alfred Douglas?
John Ruskin?

18 JULY

18 July is the birthday of two great cricketers, Dr W.G. Grace, who was born in 1848, and Sir Garfield Sobers, who was born in 1936. One English cricketer has made 118 appearances in Test cricket matches, more than any other player. What's his name?

Colin Cowdrey?
Peter May?
Freddie Trueman?
Denis Compton?

W.G. GRACE.

19 JULY

The Impressionist painter Edgar Degas was born on 19 July 1834. The Scots author A.J. Cronin was born on 19 July 1896. Cronin created *Doctor Finlay's Casebook*. When the Finlay stories were translated to television, Andrew Cruickshank played Dr Cameron and Bill Simpson played Dr Finlay. Who played their housekeeper Janet?

Barbara Murray?
Hattie Jaques?
Barbara Mullen?
June Whitfield?

20 JULY

Sir Edmund Hillary was born on 20 July 1919. The man who developed the use of radio waves as a practical means of communication, and received the Nobel Prize in 1909 for his work, died on 20 July 1937. Who was he?

Guglielmo Marconi?
E.A. Murphy?
J. Philip Reis?
Sir Joseph Swan?

21 JULY

Why did President Richard Nixon describe this week as 'the greatest week in the history of the world since the creation'? Certainly not because Ernest Hemingway was born on 21 July 1898 or because Ellen Terry died on 21 July 1928. What event in 1969 caused President Nixon to speak so?

His own election as President of the United States?
The signing of the Nuclear Test Ban Treaty?
The discovery of oil in the North Sea?
Man landing on the moon?

22 JULY

In the 'mini-Budget' of 22 July 1974 VAT was reduced to eight per cent. What do the initials VAT stand for?

Veteran Automobile Tax?
Violation of Authority in Transit?
Vanishing Amounts of Tax?
Value Added Tax?

23 JULY

An American President, Ulysses S. Grant, died on 23 July 1835. An English politician was born on 23 July 1913. With brothers called Hugh and Dingle, he is a Labour Backbencher known for his oratorical prowess. His name?

David Owen?
Michael Foot?
Edward Short?
Roy Jenkins?

24 JULY

On 24 July 1958 the first life-barons and baronesses under the Life Peerages Act were named. Anthony Wedgwood Benn was an ardent opponent of hereditary titles and campaigned for the right to be able to renounce one's own title. What was his title before he gave it up?

Viscount Cobham?
Viscount Lewisham?
Viscount Stansgate?
Viscount Linley?

25 JULY

Samuel Taylor Coleridge, the poet, died on 25 July 1834. Bertram Mills, the circus owner, was born on 25 July 1873. Where did Louis Blériot, the French airman, fly on 25 July 1909?

From Calais to Dover?
From Paris to London?
From Dublin to New York?
From New York to San Francisco?

26 JULY

Four men with remarkable minds were born on 26 July: George Bernard Shaw in 1856, Carl Jung in 1875, Aldous Huxley in 1894 and Robert Graves in 1895. Of the four, which, in *Occupation: Writer* wrote, 'As for the Freudian, it is a very low, Central European sort of humour'?

Shaw?
Jung?
Huxley?
Graves?

27 JULY

The man who created Lord Lundy, Lord Finchley, Henry King, Godolphin Horn and many other saucy scions of the aristocracy, was born on 27 July 1870. What was his name?

Harry Graham?
G.K. Chesterton?
Hilaire Belloc?
A.P. Herbert?

28 JULY

Bach died on 28 July 1750. Robespierre died on 28 July 1794. The Iron Chancellor died on 28 July 1898. Who was the Iron Chancellor?

The Duke of Wellington?
Tzar Nicholas II?
Otto von Bismarck?
Denis Healey?

29 JULY

Benito Mussolini, the Italian Fascist dictator, was born on 29 July 1883. Thirty years later to the day, Jo Grimond, the English Liberal Party Leader, was born. 29 July 1588 also saw one of the most momentous events in Britain's naval history. What was it?

> The Battle of Trafalgar?
> The defeat of the Spanish Armada?
> The launching of the *Queen Mary*?
> The departure of the *Mayflower* for America?

30 JULY

Henry Ford, pioneer of the cheap motor car, was born on 30 July 1863. Henry Moore OM was born on 30 July 1898. Moore is a sculptor. What does his OM stand for?

> Old Man?
> Order of Marlborough?
> Order of Merit?
> Old Mancunian?

31 JULY

A Hungarian composer and pianist, whose daughter Cosima married Wagner, was born in 1811 and died on 31 July 1886. What was his name?

Franz Liszt?
Gustav Mahler?
Frederic Chopin?
Robert Schumann?

1 2 3 4 5 6 7
8 9 10 11 12 13 14
15 16 17 18 19 20 21
22 23 24 25 26 27 28
29 30 31

SWITZERLAND National Flag

1 AUGUST

1 August marks the anniversary of the Battle of the Nile in 1798 and is Switzerland's Independence Day. There are four official languages in Switzerland: German, French, Italian and one other. What is the fourth?

> Swiss?
> Spanish?
> Polish?
> Romansch?

2 AUGUST

The man who invented the microphone in 1876 died on 2 August 1922. What was his name?

> Alexander Graham Bell?
> John Logie Baird?
> Benjamin Franklin?
> Thomas Alva Edison?

3 AUGUST

In his poem 'The Old Vicarage, Grantchester', Rupert Brooke, who was born on 3 August 1887, asked,

> Stands the Church clock at ten to three?
> And is there —— still for tea?

What did Brooke want to know if there was still for tea?

> Crumpet?
> Lemon curd?
> Toast?
> Honey?

4 AUGUST

Queen Elizabeth the Queen Mother was born on 4 August 1900. Who was her father?

> The Earl of Strathmore?
> Prince Andrew of Greece?
> The Duke of Cumberland?
> Lord Montagu of Beaulieu?

5 AUGUST

Guy de Maupassant, the French novelist and story writer, was born on 5 August in the year of Sir Robert Peel's death, of the Factory Act, of the Bunsen burner, of the publication of Wordsworth's *The Prelude* and of Clausius and Kelvin's exposition of the Second Law of Thermodynamics. What was the year?

> 1850?
> 1890?
> 1908?
> 1921?

6 AUGUST

The author of the play *Volpone*, which was presented at the National Theatre in 1977 with Paul Scofield and John Gielgud in the cast, died on 6 August 1637. What was his name?

Christopher Marlowe?
Ben Jonson?
Richard Brinsley Sheridan?
Oliver Goldsmith?

7 AUGUST

***August is a Wicked Month* is the title of a famous twentieth-century novel. Who wrote it?**

Margaret Drabble?
Vita Sackville-West?
Edna O'Brien?
Iris Murdoch?

8 AUGUST

The most prolific writer in the history of the world was born on 8 August 1876. His lifetime's output was in excess of seventy million words. He wrote the bulk of the schoolboy papers *The Gem* and *The Magnet* for thirty years. Charles Hamilton was his real name. How is he best known?

As Richmal Crompton?
As Frank Richards?
As Enid Blyton?
As H.E. Todd?

9 AUGUST

Léonide Massine was born on 9 August 1896. Why is he famous?

> He was a French pianist and composer?
> He was a Russian dancer and choreographer?
> He was a Dutch painter and sculptor?
> He was an English socialist and trade union leader?

10 AUGUST

The Royal Observatory at Greenwich was founded on 10 August 1675. Where is the Royal Observatory situated today?

> At Greenwich?
> At Herstmonceux?
> At Edinburgh University?
> At Broadstairs?

11 AUGUST

The English Cardinal who wrote *Apologia pro Vita Sua* and the words of the hymn 'Lead, Kindly Light', was born in 1801 and died on 11 August 1890. He founded the Oxford Movement. What was his name?

Cardinal Manning?
Cardinal Newman?
Cardinal Wolsey?
Cardinal Heenan?

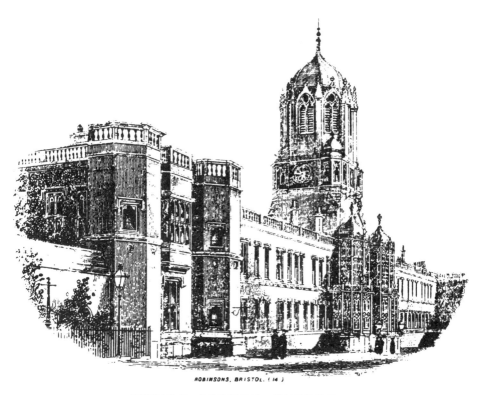

ROBINSONS, BRISTOL. (14)

CHRIST CHURCH OXFORD.

12 AUGUST

Ian Fleming, the creator of James Bond, died on 12 August 1964. Who first played Bond on the screen?

Roger Moore?
George Lazenby?
David Niven?
Sean Connery?

13 AUGUST

'Flit on, cheering angel!' was Lewis Carroll's anagram for the name of this person who died on 13 August 1910. What was the person's name?

> Frederick the Great?
> Field-Marshal Haig?
> Ferdinand Magellan?
> Florence Nightingale?

14 AUGUST

John Galsworthy, the author of *The Forsyte Saga*, was born on 14 August 1867. What happened to him in 1932?

> He died?
> He won a Nobel Prize?
> He was knighted?
> *The Forsyte Saga* was made into a television series?

15 AUGUST

Princess Anne and the Emperor Napoleon were born on 15 August, the former in 1950, the latter in 1769. The Princess married Mark Phillips. Who did the Emperor marry?

Josephine de Beauharnais?
Marie Louise of Austria?
Marlene Dietrich?
Eugénie de Montijo?

16 AUGUST

Something practical and illuminating happened to London on 16 August 1807. What was it?

The outbreak of the Great Fire?
The opening of the London Planetarium?
The introduction of gas lamps for street lighting?
The abolition of street soliciting by prostitutes?

17 AUGUST

He was born in 1712 and died on 17 August 1786. He was King of Prussia and held Silesia through the Seven Years War. He corresponded with Voltaire and played the flute. Who was he?

Wilhelm III of Prussia?
Frederick the Great?
Ethelred the Unready?
Archduke Ferdinand?

18 AUGUST

What is the origin of the name of the month of August?

It comes from the Latin word *augustinus*, meaning 'summer month'?
It is named after St Augustine, the patron saint of flowers?
It is named after the Roman Emperor Augustus?
It is the eighth month of the year and *august* means 'eight' in Latin?

19 AUGUST

The cow is of the bovine ilk;
One end is moo, the other milk.

The man who wrote that couplet was born on 19 August 1902. He was America's most delightful light versifier. What was his name?

Mark Twain?
Edward Lear?
Ogden Nash?
Cole Porter?

20 AUGUST

Lev Bronstein was assassinated in Mexico on 20 August 1940. How was he better known?

Leon Trotsky?
Lester Pearson?
Daniel Boone?
Charles Parnell?

21 AUGUST

Princess Margaret was born on 21 August 1930. By her marriage to Lord Snowdon she had two children. Where were they educated?

Privately at Kensington Palace?
At Eton College?
At Gordonstoun School?
At Bedales School?

22 AUGUST

The Red Cross was founded on 22 August 1864. When Richard III was defeated and killed at the Battle of Bosworth on 22 August 1485, he was succeeded by Henry VII. What dynasty did this Henry start?

The Tudors?
The Stuarts?
The Hanoverians?
The Windsors?

23 AUGUST

This time of the year is often called 'the silly season'. Why?

Because people go crazy over cricket and do no work?
Because the August sunshine gives people sunstroke and they become 'silly' as a consequence?
Because 23 August marks the opening of the grouse shooting season?
Because there is little 'hard news' for the press to report during the holiday season so they report a disproportionate number of 'silly' stories?

24 AUGUST

When Vesuvius erupted on 24 August AD79, two Roman towns were destroyed. One was Pompeii. What was the other?

Herculaneum?
Turin?
Cestri?
Vesuvia?

25 AUGUST

Paris was liberated on 25 August 1944. Michael Faraday, who was born in 1791, died on 25 August 1867. Who was he?

He was the physicist who founded the science of electromagnetism?
He was the church leader who founded the Mormon Faith?
He was the journalist and editor who founded *The Times*?
He was the inventor who founded the Bell Telephone Company?

26 AUGUST

The Duke of Gloucester was born on 26 August 1944. Who defeated whom at the Battle of Crécy on 26 August 1346?

Edward III defeated the French?
Louis XIII defeated the English?
Elizabeth I defeated the Spanish?
William II defeated the Dutch?

27 AUGUST

27 August marks the birth of Confucius in 551BC and the birth of a great Australian cricketer in 1908. When he was only twenty-one he scored 452 not out for New South Wales. Later he was knighted. What was his name?

D.G. Bradman?
I.M. Chappell?
R. Benaud?
K.R. Stackpole?

28 AUGUST

On 28 August 1972 a member of the Royal Family was killed in an air race crash. What was his name?

Prince Michael of Kent?
Prince William of Gloucester?
Prince Richard of Gloucester?
The Duke of Norfolk?

29 AUGUST

29 August marks the birth of the French painter Jean Ingres in 1780, and the death, in 1877, of the polygamist and Mormon leader Brigham Young. What is the name of the American city of which he was the principal founder?

Las Vegas?
Dallas?
Baltimore?
Salt Lake City?

30 AUGUST

He was born on 30 August 1871. In 1911 he announced his nuclear theory of the atom. In 1918 he succeeded in splitting the atom. In 1937 he died. What was his name?

Derek Willoughby?
Ernest Rutherford?
Colin Chapman?
Paul Watson?

31 AUGUST

John Bunyan, author of *Pilgrim's Progress*, died on 31 August 1688. Sir Bernard Lovell was born on 31 August, 1913. What is he?

A wrestler?
A poet?
An astronomer?
A zoologist?

1 2 3 4 5 6 7

8 9 10 11 12 13 14

15 16 17 18 19 20 21

22 23 24 25 26 27 28

29 30

1 SEPTEMBER

The Feast of St Giles marked the death, in 1715, of *le roi soleil* and the builder of Versailles. What was his name?

>Louis XIII?
>Louis XIV?
>Louis XV?
>Louis XVI?

2 SEPTEMBER

The Great Fire of London broke out on 2 September 1666. In which London street did it start?

>Chancery Lane?
>Park Lane?
>Pudding Lane?
>Drury Lane?

3 SEPTEMBER

Britain declared war on Germany on 3 September 1939. Oliver Cromwell declared 'My design is to make what haste I can to be gone', on 3 September 1658 and died. Who succeeded him on his death?

Richard Cromwell?
Charles II?
James I?
James II?

4 SEPTEMBER

The French Third Republic was proclaimed on 4 September in the year of the Irish Land Act, of the outbreak of the Franco-Prussian War and of the introduction in Britain of ½d. postage and stamped postcards. What year was it?

1870?
1890?
1910?
1930?

5 SEPTEMBER

On 5 September 1972 Arab guerrillas held a group of Israeli athletes hostage. The hostages, five guerrillas and a policeman were later killed in an airport gun battle. In which city did the guerrillas take the athletes hostage?

Entebbe?
Tel Aviv?
Beirut?
Munich?

6 SEPTEMBER

6 September is the anniversary of the *Mayflower's* journey in 1620, the Battle of the Marne in 1914, and the shooting of an American President in 1901. Who was he?

Andrew Johnson?
William McKinley?
Chester Arthur?
Benjamin Harrison?

7 SEPTEMBER

On 7 September 1533 Queen Elizabeth I was born. In a speech at Tilbury she declared 'I know I have the body of a weak and feeble woman, but I have the heart and stomach of a king, and of a king of England too.' What prompted this speech?

The execution of Mary Queen of Scots?
The death of her father and her accession to the throne?
The death of Lord Darnley?
The approach of the Spanish Armada?

8 SEPTEMBER

He was born on 8 September 1925. His first film was made in 1952 and called *Down Among the Z Men.* Others have included *Tom Thumb, Lolita, Dr Strangelove, A Shot in the Dark* and *There's a Girl in My Soup.* What was his name?

Kenneth Williams?
Donald Pleasence?
John Gregson?
Peter Sellers?

9 SEPTEMBER

In 1513 Scotland, in alliance with France, invaded England when Henry VIII invaded France. The result was the Battle of Flodden on 9 September. The Scots were defeated. James IV of Scotland was killed. To a Scotsman where is Auld Reekie?

Flodden?
Glasgow?
Edinburgh?
Aberdeen?

Henry VIII

10 SEPTEMBER

A referendum was held in Gibraltar on 10 September 1967. The voters were overwhelmingly in favour of Gibraltar retaining her links with Britain: 12,138 voted for — 44 voted against! What is the size of Gibraltar?

2½ square miles?
10 square miles?
100 square miles?
2,724 square miles?

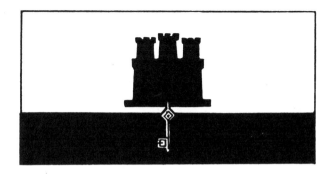

GIBRALTAR Local Flag

11 SEPTEMBER

The author of *The Rainbow, The White Peacock* and *Sons and Lovers* was born on 11 September 1885. What was his name?

D.H. Lawrence?
H.H. Munro?
H.E. Bates?
H.M. McIver?

12 SEPTEMBER

'Every Little Breeze Seems to Whisper Louise' was just one of the many successes of 'the man in the straw hat', the French singer who was born on 12 September 1888 and who became an international star. What was his name?

Yves Montand?
Sacha Distel?
Maurice Chevalier?
Charles Aznavour?

13 SEPTEMBER

At the battle of Quebec in 1759 James Wolfe led the English forces to victory. Over two hundred years later who travelled to Quebec to declare *'Vive le Québec libre!'*

Pierre Trudeau?
Georges Pompidou?
Charles de Gaulle?
Edith Piaf?

14 SEPTEMBER

Dante died on 14 September 1321. The first Duke of Wellington died on 14 September 1852. What was his name?

John Wellington?
Richard Chatham?
George Apsley?
Arthur Wellesley?

15 SEPTEMBER

Battle of Britain Day is a day for a question about the Spitfire, the fighter plane that played such a crucial part in 1940. 30 feet 4 inches long, with a wing span of 36 feet 10 inches, at 20,250 feet what was the Spitfire's maximum speed?

250mph?
375mph?
500mph?
625mph?

16 SEPTEMBER

The man who succeeded David Lloyd-George as Prime Minister on 23 October 1922 was born on 16 September 1858. What was his name?

A. Bonar Law?
Stanley Baldwin?
J. Ramsay MacDonald?
H.H. Asquith?

17 SEPTEMBER

At the time of his death on 17 September 1701, what was James II's position?

He was King of England?
He was King of England and Scotland?
He was King James VI of Scotland?
He was king of nowhere, living in exile?

18 SEPTEMBER

Tobias Smollett, who died on 17 September 1771, described Dr Johnson, who was born on 18 September 1709, as 'That great Cham of literature'. Greta Garbo was also born on 18 September, in 1905. Greta Gustafson was her real name. What was her nationality at birth?

Swedish?
Norwegian?
Danish?
American?

19 SEPTEMBER

The author of *Lord of the Flies* was born on 19 September 1911. What is his name?

John Buchan?
James Joyce?
William Golding?
J.R.R. Tolkien?

20 SEPTEMBER

A composer whose works included seven symphonies, a violin concerto and several tone poems, notably *Finlandia*, was born in 1865 and died on 20 September 1957. What was his name?

>Jean Sibelius?
>Arnold Schoenberg?
>Gustav Holst?
>Maurice Ravel?

21 SEPTEMBER

Born at Bromley in Kent on 21 September 1866, his many books included *The Time Machine, The War of the Worlds* and *The History of Mr Polly*. Anatole France once described him as 'the greatest intellectual force in the English-speaking world'. He died on 13 August 1946. What was his name?

>Arnold Bennett?
>W.W. Jacobs?
>George Orwell?
>H.G. Wells?

22 SEPTEMBER

Tunku Abdul Rahman resigned as Prime Minister of what state on 22 September 1970?

>Malaysia?
>Malawi?
>Korea?
>Ghana?

23 SEPTEMBER

Sigmund Freud died on 23 September 1939. He was born in the year that the Treaty of Paris ended the Crimean War, that Sir Henry Bessemer's converter was introduced into the steel industry, and that Flaubert's *Madame Bovary* was published. What year was it?

>1842?
>1856?
>1866?
>1876?

24 SEPTEMBER

Sir Alan Herbert, famous for his *Misleading Cases*, was born on 24 September 1890. Horace Walpole was also born on 24 September, but in 1717. Why is he famous?

He was the first English Prime Minister?
He was a writer, wit and bachelor?
He was a composer who wrote 'Rule Britannia'?
He was a scientist?

25 SEPTEMBER

Today is the day on which Samuel Pepys drank his very first cup of tea in 1660. In which year did the notorious Boston Tea Party take place?

1660?
1773?
1776?
1804?

26 SEPTEMBER

**On 26 September 1875 John Buchan was born. On 26
September 1888 T. S. Eliot was born. On 26
September 1897 Giovanni Battista Montini was born.
In later years, how was he better known?**

As Perry Como?
As Mussolini?
As Fernandel?
As Pope Paul VI?

27 SEPTEMBER

**27 September marks the death of Edward II in 1327,
the death of the painter Degas in 1917 and the start of
the Stockton to Darlington Railway in 1825. What
speed did Stephenson's locomotive *Locomotion*
achieve on this occasion?**

10 mph?
15 mph?
20 mph?
30 mph?

28 SEPTEMBER

The French chemist, who was born at Dôle in the Jura in 1822, whose researches on fermentation led to the science of bacteriology and whose investigations into infectious diseases and their prevention to the science of immunology, died on 28 September 1895. What was his name?

Jacques Prévert?
Jean de la Tour?
Georges Canton?
Louis Pasteur?

29 SEPTEMBER

Horatio Nelson was born on 29 September 1758. What was the name of his mistress?

Caroline Lamb?
Kitty O'Shea?
Emma Hamilton?
Rachel Carstairs?

The *Victory*, Nelson's flagship

30 SEPTEMBER

Lord Raglan was born on 30 September 1788. The French tragic dramatist whose masterpieces include *Le Cid* and *Rodogune* died on 30 September 1684. What was his name?

Marivaux?
Corneille?
Racine?
Rostand?

1 2 3 4 5 6 7

8 9 10 11 12 13 14

15 16 17 18 19 20 21

22 23 24 25 26 27 28

29 30 31

1 OCTOBER

Today is the National Day of Nigeria. What is its capital?

> Lagos?
> Addis Ababa?
> Libreville?
> Abidjan?

2 OCTOBER

Richard III was born on 2 October 1452. Graham Greene was born on 2 October 1904. The first match of a particular sport to be played at Twickenham, Middlesex, took place on 2 October 1909. What is the sport called?

> Netball?
> Squash Rackets?
> Rugby Union Football?
> Bowls?

3 OCTOBER

William Morris, poet, craftsman, socialist, died on 3 October in the year that the first modern Olympic Games were held in Athens. What year was it?

1860?
1896?
1912?
1934?

4 OCTOBER

Today is the Feast Day of the St Francis who founded the Franciscan Order. He was said to have received the stigmata in 1224. He was canonised in 1228. Which St Francis was he?

St Francis Xavier?
St Francis Solano?
St Francis Borgia?
St Francis of Assisi?

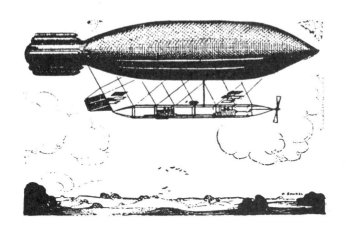

5 OCTOBER

When the airship R101 crashed on 5 October 1930 where was it travelling to?

> The United States?
> France?
> Egypt?
> India?

6 OCTOBER

Alfred Lord Tennyson died on 6 October in 1892, the year in which a very famous Liberal statesman became Prime Minister for the fourth and last time. What was his name?

> William Ewart Gladstone?
> Benjamin Disraeli?
> The Marquess of Salisbury?
> The Earl of Roseberry?

7 OCTOBER

When this great music hall star tottered onto the stage on Wednesday 4 October 1922 and sang 'I'm one of the ruins Cromwell knocked about a bit' for the very last time, it was clear to the audience that the knocking about had indeed been severe. Three days later, on 7 October, she died. Who was she?

> Vesta Tilley?
> Florrie Forde?
> Marie Lloyd?
> Marie Loftus?

8 OCTOBER

Henry Fielding, who died on 8 October 1754, wrote *Tom Jones* and *Joseph Andrews*, novels that were turned into films in 1963 and 1977. Who directed both films?

> Alfred Hitchcock?
> Franco Zeffirelli?
> Tony Richardson?
> John Schlesinger?

9 OCTOBER

Lord Hailsham of St Marylebone was born on 9 October 1907. His grandfather, Quintin Hogg, was an educationalist and philanthropist who made a major contribution to general education in 1882. What was it?

> He started the 11+ examination system?
> He reorganised the London Polytechnic?
> He founded Bristol University?
> He started co-educational secondary schools?

10 OCTOBER

The composer who created *Il Trovatore, Aida, Otello* and *Falstaff* (which was produced when he was eighty) was born near Busseto in the province of Parma on 10 October 1813. What was his name?

Giuseppe Verdi?
Charles Gounod?
Georges Bizet?
Anton Dvorak?

11 OCTOBER

On 11 October 1968 the Americans successfully launched *Apollo 7*, the first flight of the three-man capsule designed eventually to travel to the moon. When Neil Armstrong became the first man to step onto the moon's surface in 1969, who were the other two men with him on the mission?

Edwin Aldrin and Michael Collins?
James McDivitt and David Scott?
Alan Shepard and Edgar Mitchell?
James Irwin and Alfred Worden?

12 OCTOBER

'I realise that patriotism is not enough. I must have no hatred or bitterness towards anyone.' Whose last words were these, spoken on 12 October 1915?

> Rupert Brooke?
> Wilfred Owen?
> Edith Cavell?
> Earl Haig?

13 OCTOBER

On 13 October 1905 Sir Henry Irving, the great actor-manager, died. Twenty years later to the day Margaret Thatcher was born. How many children does Mrs Thatcher have?

> None?
> One?
> One set of twins?
> Three?

14 OCTOBER

14 October marks the anniversary of the Battle of Hastings in 1066, the birth of James II in 1633 and the birth, in 1890, of Dwight Eisenhower, American General and President. Who was President Eisenhower's Vice-President?

> Spiro Agnew?
> Gerald Ford?
> Hubert Humphrey?
> Richard Nixon?

15 OCTOBER

15 October is the birthday of three distinguished men of letters. C.P. Snow was born in 1905. P.G. Wodehouse was born in 1856. The man who said 'I can resist everything except temptation', and 'Truth is never pure and rarely simple', was born in 1856. What was his name?

George Bernard Shaw?
Max Beerbohm?
Arthur Wing Pinero?
Oscar Wilde?

16 OCTOBER

The executions following the Nuremberg Trials took place on 16 October 1946. In what part of Germany is Nuremberg?

Bavaria?
Rhineland?
Hamburg?
Lower Saxony?

17 OCTOBER

Before he died at the Battle of Zutphen on 17 October 1586, Sir Philip Sidney passed a cup of water to another man and said, 'Thy necessity is greater than mine.' Why is Sir Philip Sidney still famous?

Because he brought the potato to Europe?
Because of his poetry?
Because he wooed and almost won Elizabeth I?
Because he was a heroic general?

18 OCTOBER

Today is the Feast Day of St Luke, one of the apostles. Apart from the Gospel according to St Luke, which of the books of the Bible is he believed to have written?

The Acts of the Apostles?
Corinthians?
Revelation?
Timothy?

19 OCTOBER

When Jonathan Swift died on 19 October 1745, he was known as Dean Swift. Of which Cathedral did he become Dean in 1714?

Saint Paul's in London?
Canterbury Cathedral?
Saint Patrick's in Dublin?
Durham Cathedral?

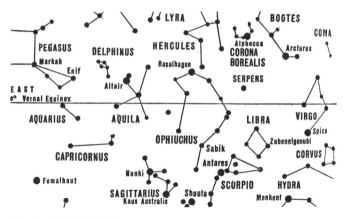

LYRA
BOÖTES
COMA
PEGASUS   DELPHINUS   HERCULES   Alphecca   Arcturus
Markab   CORONA
Enif   Rasalhague   BOREALIS
EAST   Altair   SERPENS
0° Vernal Equinox
AQUARIUS   AQUILA   LIBRA   VIRGO
                                                      Spica
                            OPHIUCHUS   Zubenelgenubi
CAPRICORNUS   Sabik   CORVUS
                            Antares
● Fomalhaut   Nunki   HYDRA
                SAGITTARIUS   Shoula   SCORPIO   Menkent
     ?   Kaus Australis

20 OCTOBER

He was professor of mathematics at Gresham College, London, and professor of astronomy at Oxford, but he is best known as the man who built and rebuilt so many of London's churches and other great buildings after the Great Fire. He was born on 20 October 1632. His name?

Inigo Jones?
John Flamsteed?
Christopher Wren?
Frank Lloyd Wright?

21 OCTOBER

Alfred Nobel, inventor of dynamite and founder of the Nobel prizes, was born on 21 October 1833, the anniversary of the Battle of Trafalgar in 1805. Glaser, Alvarez, Gabor, Hewish, Ryle, Rainwater, Bohr and Mottelson are the names of recent Nobel prize winners in which discipline?

Physics?
Chemistry?
Physiology and Medicine?
Literature?

22 OCTOBER

Sarah Bernhardt, the great French tragedienne, was born on 22 October 1845. In 1977 a film was released about her life. Who starred in the film?

Maggie Smith?
Glenda Jackson?
Dorothy Tutin?
Penelope Keith?

23 OCTOBER

The Battle of El Alamein was fought on 23 October 1942. What was the first name of Viscount Montgomery of Alamein?

George?
David?
Bernard?
Richard?

24 OCTOBER

The original William Hickey died on 24 October 1875. In which British newspaper today will you find the William Hickey gossip column?

Daily Mirror?
Daily Mail?
Daily Express?
Daily Telegraph?

172

25 OCTOBER

25 October marks the anniversary of the Battle of Agincourt in 1415 and the death of Chaucer in 1400. The composer of 'The Blue Danube' and four hundred other waltzes was born on 25 October 1825. What was his name?

> Johann Strauss the elder?
> Johann Strauss the younger?
> Josef Strauss?
> Eduard Strauss?

26 OCTOBER

The Erie Canal, the 360-mile waterway from Albany to Buffalo, was opened on 25 October 1825. On 26 October 1764, the satirical artist and engraver famous for his *Rake's Progress* died. What was his name?

> William Blake?
> William Hogarth?
> George Romney?
> Edward Burne-Jones?

27 OCTOBER

The man after whom the Teddy Bear was named was born on 27 October 1858. What was his name?

Edward VII?
Theodore Roosevelt?
Edward Kennedy?
Teddy Johnson?

28 OCTOBER

Captain Cook was born on 28 October 1728 and John Locke died on 28 October 1704. Locke was an English liberal philosopher who founded empiricism. In a nutshell, what is the basis of the doctrine of empiricism?

That all knowledge is derived from experience?
That it is in the nature of man to want to expand his empire?
That there is no life after death?
That there is no such thing as 'absolute truth'?

29 OCTOBER

Sir Walter Raleigh, adventurer, writer and the man responsible for introducing potatoes and tobacco to England, died in 1618. How?

He was killed in a riding accident?
He died of the pox?
He was executed?
He was killed while fighting the Spanish?

30 OCTOBER

Feodor Dostoyevsky, the Russian novelist, was born on 30 October 1821. Richard Brinsley Sheridan, the Irish playwright, was born on 30 October 1751. There is a character in his play *The Rivals* whose name is now used to describe a particular verbal slip. What is it?

Spoonerism?
Archaism?
Malapropism?
Neologism?

175

31 OCTOBER

A question about witches for Hallowe'en. The American playwright Arthur Miller wrote a play about the persecution of the so-called Salem witches. What was the play called?

The Witches?
The Crucible?
Darkness at Noon?
Blithe Spirit?

1 2 3 4 5 6 7
8 9 10 11 12 13 14
15 16 17 18 19 20 21
22 23 24 25 26 27 28
29 30

1 NOVEMBER

Ezra Pound died on 1 November 1972. Why was he famous?

> He redesigned all British banknotes in 1948?
> He designed Concorde?
> He was a poet?
> He was President Truman's Secretary of State?

2 NOVEMBER

Following a fall which fractured his leg while he was cutting a branch of a tree in his garden, George Bernard Shaw died at the age of 94 on 2 November 1950. Where did he live during his last years?

> Rye in Sussex?
> Ayot St Lawrence in Hertfordshire?
> Wembley in Middlesex?
> Petersfield in Hampshire?

3 NOVEMBER

It was on 3 November 1871 that Henry Stanley declared 'Dr Livingstone, I presume?' when he discovered the missionary and explorer at Ujiji. Where is Kigoma–Ujiji now?

> Tanzania?
> Uganda?
> South Africa?
> Niger?

4 NOVEMBER

His incidental music for *A Midsummer Night's Dream* includes a Wedding March that has been played at countless weddings. He died on 4 November 1847. Who was he?

> Alexander Borodin?
> Gabriel Fauré?
> John Ireland?
> Felix Mendelssohn?

5 NOVEMBER

***Why* did Guy Fawkes and his fellow conspirators plan the gunpowder plot in 1605?**

> Because they were angry about the treatment of Catholics?
> Because they wanted James I to marry a Dutch princess?
> Because Guy Fawkes' father had been executed in 1604?
> Because they were in the pay of the French?

6 NOVEMBER

Peter Tchaikovsky, the Russian composer, died on 6 November 1893. When Ken Russell made a film of the life of the composer, who played the part of Tchaikovsky?

> Oliver Reed?
> Richard Chamberlain?
> Alec McCowen?
> Michael Caine?

7 NOVEMBER

Marie Curie was born on 7 November 1867. Cardinal Heenan died on 7 November 1975. Who succeeded him as Cardinal Archbishop of Westminster?

> Trevor Huddleston?
> David Shepherd?
> Tom Driberg?
> Basil Hume?

8 NOVEMBER

Two great writers died today. One was Milton, who died in 1674. The other was the author of *War and Peace*, who died in 1910. What was his name?

> Emile Zola?
> Ernest Hemingway?
> Leo Tolstoy?
> Feodor Dostoyevsky?

9 NOVEMBER

'Eighteen straight whiskies, I think that is the record,' are reputed to be the last words of this poet who died on 9 November 1953 in New York. What was his name?

W.H. Auden?
Robert Lowell?
Philip Larkin?
Dylan Thomas?

10 NOVEMBER

Martin Luther was born on 10 November 1483. Catherine the Great died on 10 November 1796. She was Empress Catherine II — but of where?

Prussia?
Russia?
Austria?
The Holy Roman Empire?

11 NOVEMBER

Today was Armistice Day in 1918. There was a film about the Great War called *Oh, what a Lovely War!* Who directed it?

Joan Littlewood?
Lindsay Anderson?
John Ford?
Richard Attenborough?

12 NOVEMBER

Two female novelists died on 12 November. One was Mrs Gaskell, who died in 1865. The other was the author of *The Scarlet Pimpernel*, who died in 1947. What was her name?

Elizabeth Bowen?
Nadine Gordimer?
Doris Lessing?
Emma Orczy?

13 NOVEMBER

R.C. Sherriff, who was born in 1896 and who died on 13 November 1975, wrote a play about the First World War which was produced in 1929 (with Laurence Olivier in the cast). What was the play called?

Long Day's Journey Into Night?
Sleuth?
Journey's End?
Chips With Everything?

14 NOVEMBER

The Earl of Chester, Duke of Rothesay, Earl of Carrick and Baron Renfrew are all one person. He was born on 14 November 1948. What is his best-known title?

The Duke of Edinburgh?
The Prince of Wales?
The Duke of Gloucester?
The Duke of Kent?

15 NOVEMBER

The British socialist leader who was architect of the National Health Service that came into operation in 1940, was born on 15 November 1897. What was his name?

Aneurin Bevan?
Ernest Bevin?
Stafford Cripps?
Harold Wilson?

16 NOVEMBER

The 'king' of Hollywood, with big ears and an impudent grin, whose first film was *The Painted Desert* in 1930 and whose last was *The Misfits* in 1960, died on 16 November 1960. What was his name?

Humphrey Bogart?
Clark Gable?
George Sanders?
Anthony Quinn?

17 NOVEMBER

Ferdinand de Lesseps's great masterwork was opened on 17 November 1869. What was it?

The London Palladium?
The Empire State Building in New York?
The Aswan Dam?
The Suez Canal?

18 NOVEMBER

Sir William Schwenk Gilbert, best known as the lyricist for the famous Gilbert and Sullivan light operas, was born in 1836. Before working with Sullivan, he became famous in his own right for his collection of comic verses. What were they called?

Cautionary Tales?
Odd Odes?
Bab Ballads?
Nonsense Songs?

19 NOVEMBER

Charles I was born on 19 November 1600. Schubert died on 19 November 1828. What does the musical term *adagio* mean ?

Very slow?
Very fast?
Tearfully?
Very loud?

20 NOVEMBER

The Queen was married on 20 November 1947. Queen Alexandra died on 20 November 1925. Robert Kennedy was born on 20 November 1925. What office did he hold in his brother John's administration?

Vice-President?
Secretary of State?
Attorney-General?
Special Counsel to the President?

21 NOVEMBER

Q was born on 21 November 1863. Who was he?

Quasimodo?
Sir Arthur Quiller-Couch?
Ian Fleming?
Peter Quennell?

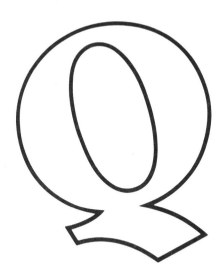

22 NOVEMBER

George Eliot, the novelist, was born on 22 November 1819. President J.F. Kennedy was assassinated on 22 November 1963. The day is the Feast of St Cecilia. Since the sixteenth century she has been regarded as the patron saint of which group of people?

Sailors?
Beggars?
Musicians?
Bakers?

23 NOVEMBER

Perkin Warbeck died on 23 November 1499. Why is he famous?

He was a Flemish impostor who claimed to be the younger son of Edward IV?
He was an English printer who printed the first English Bible?
He was a Scottish nobleman who wrote 'Auld Lang Syne'?
He was a Welsh sailor who first discovered the Isle of Ely?

24 NOVEMBER

Laurence Sterne was one of the first of the major English novelists. He was born on 24 November 1713. He is remembered chiefly for two works: one is *A Sentimental Journey*. What is the other?

Moll Flanders?
Tristram Shandy?
Roderick Random?
Robinson Crusoe?

25 NOVEMBER

Isaac Watts was born in 1674 and died on 25 November 1748. Why is he famous?

He wrote hymns?
He invented the steam engine?
He developed a primitive form of radar?
He was an early physiotherapist?

26 NOVEMBER

On 26 November 1966 there was a General Election in New Zealand and Keith Holyoake was returned as Prime Minister. On the same day, there was another General Election in another country and Harold Holt was returned as Prime Minister. What was the country?

Canada?
New Guinea?
Jamaica?
Australia?

N.Z. Government Flag and Jack

27 NOVEMBER

The man responsible for the centigrade thermometer was born on 27 November 1701. What was his name?

Anders Celsius?
Gabriel Fahrenheit?
Cedric Grade?
John Calvin?

190

28 NOVEMBER

'Tyger! Tyger! burning bright' is the opening line of a poem by a poet, painter and dreamer of dreams who was born on 28 November 1757. What was his name?

Samuel Taylor Coleridge?
William Wordsworth?
William Blake?
Matthew Prior?

29 NOVEMBER

He was world motor racing champion in 1962 and 1968. He was killed on 29 November 1975. What was his name?

Jack Brabham?
John Surtees?
Graham Hill?
Jackie Stewart?

30 NOVEMBER

The Feast of Saint Andrew was the birthday of Winston Churchill in 1874 and of Samuel Clemens in 1835. How was Clemens better known?

As Hopalong Cassidy?
As Baron Munchausen?
As Mark Twain?
As Augustus John?

1 2 3 4 5 6 7

8 9 10 11 12 13 14

15 16 17 18 19 20 21

22 23 24 25 26 27 28

29 30 31

1 DECEMBER

Queen Alexandra, wife of Edward VII, was born on 1 December 1844, the date of Henry I's death in 1135. Before her marriage, of which country was Alexandra a Princess?

        Austria?
        Hungary?
        Denmark?
        Greece?

2 DECEMBER

The Marquis de Sade died on 2 December 1814. A sadist enjoys inflicting pain. What does a masochist enjoy?

        Inflicting pain on animals?
        Receiving pain?
        The company of corpses?
        Inflicting pain on several people at the same time?

3 DECEMBER

Robert Louis Stevenson, who was born on 13 November 1850 and died on 3 December 1894, wrote *Treasure Island*, featuring that most rascally of pirates, Long John Silver. On the good ship *Hispaniola*, what was Long John Silver's rank?

        First Lieutenant?
        Ship's Doctor?
        Bosun?
        Ship's Cook?

4 DECEMBER

On 4 December 1957 ninety people were killed in a railway accident in the fog. It was one of the worst railway disasters of all time. Where did it occur?

Lewisham?
New York?
Accrington?
New Delhi?

5 DECEMBER

In one of his most ambitious cartoon films, Walt Disney, who was born on 5 December 1901, combined cartoon characters with classical music. The year was 1940. What was the film called?

One Hundred and One Dalmations?
The Jungle Book?
Bambi?
Fantasia?

6 DECEMBER

According to tradition, tonight's the night on which St Nicholas travels the world giving presents to all the good children, accompanied by a fearsome character who gives a beating to all the bad children. What is St Nicholas's cruel companion called?

> Captain Hook?
> Bluebeard?
> Black Peter?
> Old Nick?

7 DECEMBER

On 7 December 1941 the Japanese made a surprise attack on Pearl Harbour, a major United States naval and air base, so precipitating America's involvement in the Second World War. Where is Pearl Harbour?

> On the South coast of a Hawaiian island?
> On the West coast of a South American island?
> On the North coast of a West Indian island?
> On the East bank of the Panama Canal?

8 DECEMBER

The composer Sibelius was born on 8 December 1865, so today's a good day for a musical question. What is the term that describes the lowest register of the female voice?

> Mezzo Soprano?
> Baritone?
> Moderato?
> Contralto?

9 DECEMBER

On 9 December 1962, the anniversary of the birth of the poet John Milton in 1608, Tanganyika became a republic. Who was the republic's first president?

> Milton Obote?
> Julius Nyerere?
> Kwame Nkrumah?
> Idi Amin?

10 DECEMBER

Earl Alexander of Tunis was born on 10 December 1891. What was his first name?

> Montagu?
> Harold?
> James?
> William?

11 DECEMBER

Alexander Solzhenitsyn, Russian novelist and Nobel Prize winner in 1970, was born on 11 December 1918. In what year was he expelled from the Soviet Union?

1970?
1972?
1974?
1976?

12 DECEMBER

Robert Browning, the English poet, died on 12 December 1889. The French novelist who wrote *Madame Bovary* was born on 12 December 1821. What was his name?

Victor Hugo?
Gustave Flaubert?
Benjamin Constant?
Stendhal?

13 DECEMBER

The Aga Kahn IV was born on 13 December in the year that Amy Mollison flew from England to Cape Town in three days and six hours and Germany reoccupied the Rhineland. What year was it?

> 1933?
> 1936?
> 1939?
> 1941?

14 DECEMBER

George VI was born at York Cottage, Sandringham, on 14 December 1895. On what date did he die?

> 1 March 1950?
> 2 September 1951?
> 6 February 1952?
> 2 June 1953?

15 DECEMBER

The deaths of three memorable men took place on 15 December. Jan Vermeer, the Dutch painter, died in 1675. Grigori Rasputin, the monk at the court of Tsar Nicholas II, died in 1916. And Isaak Walton died in 1683. Why is he famous?

> He invented the fountain pen?
> He was an actor and friend of Shakespeare?
> He wrote *The Compleat Angler?*
> He produced the first atlas of the world?

16 DECEMBER

On 16 December 1770 Beethoven was born. On 16 December 1775 Jane Austen was born. In the 1940 film of her novel _Pride and Prejudice_, who played the parts of Elizabeth and Darcy?

> Greer Garson and Laurence Olivier?
> Vivien Leigh and Clark Gable?
> Katherine Hepburn and Spencer Tracy?
> Elizabeth Taylor and Richard Burton?

17 DECEMBER

Simon Bolivar was born in 1783 and died on 17 December 1830. Who was he?

> He was the man who designed the Panama Canal?
> He was a South American revolutionary?
> He was a Spanish poet and playwright?
> He was the man who isolated the influenza germ?

18 DECEMBER

Christopher Fry, the English playwright, was born on 18 December 1907. So was the original Clown, Joey, in 1779. What was his full name?

Joseph Chamberlain?
Joseph Cotten?
Joseph Leno?
Joseph Grimaldi?

19 DECEMBER

Queen Edith died on 19 December 1075. To whom was she married?

Edward the Confessor?
William the Conqueror?
Harold II?
Stephen?

20 DECEMBER

Sir Robert Menzies, who was born on 20 December 1894, was Australia's longest-serving Prime Minister. He retired in 1966. In which year did he first become Australian Premier?

1939?
1949?
1959?
1961?

21 DECEMBER

What happened to General Charles de Gaulle on 1 December 1958?

He was defeated in a national referendum?
He was elected President of France?
He was the victim of an assassination attempt?
He was married for the third time?

22 DECEMBER

Mary Ann Evans, the author of *Adam Bede* and *Daniel Deronda*, was born on 22 November 1819 and died on 22 December 1880. How was she better known?

As George Sand?
As Emily Dickinson?
As Jane Austen?
As George Eliot?

23 DECEMBER

Captain Cook discovered Christmas Island in 1777. In which Ocean is the island situated?

The Indian Ocean?
The Pacific Ocean?
The Atlantic Ocean?
The Arctic Ocean?

24 DECEMBER

Colin Cowdrey, the England cricketer, was born on 24 December 1932. Vasco da Gama, the Portuguese navigator, died on 24 December 1524. By doubling the Cape of Good Hope, he discovered the sea route to which major country in 1498?

America?
Peru?
India?
China?

25 DECEMBER

In which year is it now generally believed that Jesus was born?

In the year 0?
In 4 BC?
In AD 1?
In AD 4?

26 DECEMBER

In which year was the Queen's Christmas Day broadcast first shown on television?

1953?
1955?
1957?
1964?

27 DECEMBER

Louis Pasteur, the great French scientist, was born on 27 December 1822. Jack Benny, the great American comedian, died on 27 December 1974. Generous to a fault, he was famous for his meanness. An excellent violin player, he was noted for his poor fiddling. In his long-running television series, what was the name given to his black manservant?

Winchester?
Chichester?
Manchester?
Rochester?

28 DECEMBER

On 28 December 1972 the Duke of Windsor died in Paris. Of his seven Christian names, which one did he use as his first name?

> Edward?
> Albert?
> Andrew?
> David?

29 DECEMBER

'You cannot fight against the future. Time is on our side.' So said the man who was born on 29 December 1809 at the time of the Reform Bill in 1866. What was his name?

> Sir Robert Peel?
> W.E. Gladstone?
> George Canning?
> Earl Grey?

30 DECEMBER

Rudyard Kipling was born on 30 December 1865. Pablo Casals, who was born on 30 December 1876 and who died in 1973, was the son of an organist. What was his own instrument?

> The piano?
> The violin?
> The cello?
> The banjo?

31 DECEMBER

Today is New Year's Eve and tomorrow is New Year's Day. (31 December is also the birthday of the painter Henri Matisse in 1869 and of the cricketer Peter May in 1929.) In which years in the twentieth century have New Year's Eve and New Year's Day fallen in the same year?

1901?
1945?
None?
All?

Answers

H

1. 365.2422 days
2. 1759
3. Josiah Wedgwood
4. Albert Camus
5. Calvin Coolidge
6. 1920
7. The horse
8. Isaac Newton
9. Napoleon I's brother Louis
10. Sam Colt
11. Thomas Hardy
12. Agatha Christie
13. *Exiles*
14. John Flamsteed
15. Martin Luther King
16. *The Decline and Fall of the Roman Empire*
17. 1916-1922
18. Muhammad Ali
19. Paul Cézanne
20. His Silver Jubilee in 1935
21. George Orwell
22. Byron
23. Charles Kingsley
24. AD 76-138
25. W. Somerset Maugham
26. Tasmania
27. John Logie Baird demonstrated his first television pictures
28. Charlemagne
29. French
30. Charles I and Mahatma Gandhi
31. Schubert

1. Stanley Matthews
2. George Thomas
3. Woodrow Wilson
4. One was an author and the other an actor
5. Sir Robert Peel
6. North Island
7. Charles Dickens
8. He was an art critic
9. James I
10. Harold Macmillan
11. The first crossing of the Antarctic continent
12. Abraham Lincoln
13. Maigret
14. William Shakespeare
15. He was a cartoonist
16. He was an historian
17. Sir Donald Wolfit
18. Martin Luther
19. Nicolas Copernicus
20. A philosopher
21. *Dead Souls*
22. George Washington
23. 1660-1669
24. Thomas Bowdler
25. The Campaign for Nuclear Disarmament
26. Victor Hugo
27. His diary
28. Ladysmith was a town in South Africa besieged during the Boer War
29. Bissextile

1. St George's Channel
2. 1960
3. He founded the Promenade Concerts
4. 1824
5. As Stalin
6. Michelangelo
7. For designing the lions in Trafalgar Square
8. London
9. *Vostok 1*
10. He founded the Russian Ballet
11. Sir Harold Wilson
12. His *Brief Lives*
13. 1923
14. Albert Einstein
15. The Lyttelton
16. The formation of the social services
17. Twenty-six
18. Sir Robert Walpole
19. *The Arabian Nights*
20. Ibsen
21. Bach
22. As writers
23. 1954
24. He illustrated *Winnie the Pooh*
25. He was a composer
26. Blenheim Palace
27. April 1976
28. George V
29. It was sold to the United States by Russia
30. It was stolen from the National Gallery and not recovered until 1965
31. He was Dean of St Paul's

1. APRIL FOOL!
   Ephraim Bomquist
   and his tea-cup never
   existed.
2. Sir Alec Guinness
3. Richard D'Oyly Carte
4. *The Golden Hind*
5. Algernon Charles
   Swinburne
6. Florence
7. William Wordsworth
8. Pablo Picasso
9. Isambard Kingdom
   Brunel
10. Viscount Palmerston
11. The War of the
    Spanish Succession
12. Harry Truman
13. 4
14. Sir Ralph Richardson
15. She collided with an
    iceberg.
16. *The Great Dictator*
17. Mary Queen of Scots
18. Lord Jeffreys
19. He was an actor-
    manager
20. The Eiffel Tower in
    Paris
21. At 17 Bruton Street,
    London W.1
22. Albert Finney
23. Richard Burbage
24. Anthony Trollope
25. Australian and New
    Zealand Army Corps
26. He took up residence
    at 10 Downing
    Street
27. ....
28. He was shot while
    attempting to escape
    to Switzerland
29. Captain Bligh
30. Lockheed

1. Zambia
2. Nancy Astor
3. The Festival of Britain
4. Nigel Dempster
5. A palindrome
6. Sigmund Freud
7. SS *Lusitania*
8. Harry S. Truman
9. England 4 Germany 2
10. Ujiji in 1871
11. Irving Berlin
12. Florence Nightingale
13. Gary Cooper
14. 212 degrees
15. Alan Badel
16. H.E. Bates
17. Jo Grimond
18. Dame Margot Fonteyn
19. T.E. Lawrence
20. Christopher Columbus
21. Alexander Pope
22. Vivien Leigh
23. He founded the Standard Oil Company
24. HMS *Hood*
25. Richard Dimbleby
26. Samuel Pepys
27. Henry Kissinger
28. Governor of the Bahamas
29. Charles I and Henrietta-Maria of France
30. Voltaire
31. 1916

1. Ben Jonson
2. Pilt Down
3. The line above which no ship must sink while loading
4. Frank Finlay
5. A balloon
6. Over 4000
7. Robert Bruce
8. He was an artist
9. *Rocket*
10. Prince Andrew of Greece and Princess Alice of Battenberg
11. 1776
12. Avon
13. Rugby
14. John Logie Baird
15. 16 hours 12 minutes
16. The Battle of Dettingen
17. China
18. Belgium
19. James I
20. *The Prince*
21. Brazil
22. Puccini
23. Isaac Singer
24. Edward II
25. General Custer
26. Trygve Lie
27. She overcame overwhelming physical handicaps, including deafness and blindness, to become an author and lecturer
28. The Allies and Germany
29. He was a great pianist *and* he was the first Prime Minister of modern Poland
30. Wimpole Street

1. Around 20 million
2. 1963
3. Syria
4. Philadelphia
5. She was a novelist
6. 1685
7. 1930
8. Percy Bysshe Shelley
9. Edward Heath
10. Clerihew
11. A Dutch Renaissance humanist and author of *Praise of Folly*
12. 1935
13. Charlotte Corday
14. He was a clown
15. If it rains on St Swithin's Day it will rain for the next forty days
16. He beat Scott in the race to reach the South Pole in 1911
17. James McNeill Whistler
18. Colin Cowdrey
19. Barbara Mullen
20. Guglielmo Marconi
21. Man landing on the moon
22. Value Added Tax
23. Michael Foot
24. Viscount Stansgate
25. From Calais to Dover
26. Graves
27. Hilaire Belloc
28. Otto von Bismarck
29. The defeat of the Spanish Armada
30. Order of Merit
31. Franz Liszt

1. Romansch
2. Alexander Graham Bell
3. Honey
4. The Earl of Strathmore
5. 1850
6. Ben Jonson
7. Edna O'Brien
8. As Frank Richards
9. He was a Russian dancer and choreographer
10. At Herstmonceux
11. Cardinal Newman
12. Sean Connery
13. Florence Nightingale
14. He won a Nobel Prize
15. Josephine de Beauharnais first, then Marie Louise of Austria
16. The introduction of gas lamps for street lighting
17. Frederick the Great
18. It is named after the Roman Emperor Augustus
19. Ogden Nash
20. Leon Trotsky
21. At Bedales School
22. The Tudors
23. Because there is little 'hard news' for the press to report during the holiday season
24. Herculaneum
25. He was the physicist who founded the science of electro-magnetism
26. Edward III defeated the French
27. D.G. Bradman
28. Prince William of Gloucester
29. Salt Lake City
30. Ernest Rutherford
31. An astronomer

1. Louis XIV
2. Pudding Lane
3. Richard Cromwell
4. 1870
5. Munich
6. William McKinley
7. The approach of the Spanish Armada
8. Peter Sellers
9. Edinburgh
10. 2½ square miles
11. D.H. Lawrence
12. Maurice Chevalier
13. Charles de Gaulle
14. Arthur Wellesley
15. 375mph
16. A. Bonar Law
17. He was king of nowhere, living in exile
18. Swedish
19. William Golding
20. Jean Sibelius
21. H.G. Wells
22. Malaysia
23. 1856
24. He was a writer, wit and bachelor
25. 1773
26. As Pope Paul VI
27. 15mph
28. Louis Pasteur
29. Emma Hamilton
30. Corneille

1. Lagos
2. Rugby Union Football
3. 1896
4. St Francis of Assisi
5. India
6. William Ewart Gladstone
7. Marie Lloyd
8. Tony Richardson
9. He reorganised the London Polytechnic.
10. Giuseppe Verdi
11. Edwin Aldrin and Michael Collins
12. Edith Cavell
13. One set of twins
14. Richard Nixon
15. Oscar Wilde
16. Bavaria
17. Because of his poetry
18. The Acts of the Apostles
19. Saint Patrick's in Dublin
20. Christopher Wren
21. Physics
22. Glenda Jackson
23. Bernard
24. *Daily Express*
25. Johann Strauss the younger
26. William Hogarth
27. Theodore Roosevelt
28. That all knowledge is derived from experience
29. He was executed
30. Malapropism
31. *The Crucible*

1. He was a poet
2. Ayot St Lawrence in Hertfordshire
3. Tanzania
4. Felix Mendelssohn
5. Because they were angry about the treatment of the Catholics
6. Richard Chamberlain
7. Basil Hume
8. Leo Tolstoy
9. Dylan Thomas
10. Russia
11. Richard Attenborough
12. Emma Orczy
13. *Journey's End*
14. The Prince of Wales
15. Aneurin Bevan
16. Clark Gable
17. The Suez Canal
18. *Bab Ballads*
19. Very slow
20. Attorney-General
21. Sir Arthur Quiller-Couch
22. Musicians
23. He was a Flemish impostor who claimed to be the younger son of Edward IV
24. *Tristram Shandy*
25. He wrote hymns
26. Australia
27. Anders Celsius
28. William Blake
29. Graham Hill
30. Mark Twain

1. Denmark
2. Receiving pain
3. Ship's Cook
4. Lewisham
5. *Fantasia*
6. Black Peter
7. On the South coast of a Hawaiian island
8. Contralto
9. Julius Nyerere
10. Harold
11. 1974
12. Gustave Flaubert
13. 1936
14. 6 February 1952
15. He wrote *The Compleat Angler*.
16. Greer Garson and Laurence Olivier
17. He was a South American revolutionary
18. Joseph Grimaldi
19. Edward the Confessor
20. 1939
21. He was elected President of France
22. As George Eliot
23. The Pacific Ocean
24. India
25. In 4BC
26. 1957
27. Rochester
28. David
29. W.E. Gladstone
30. The cello
31. All!